Solutions Manual for

Mathematics of Investment and Credit

 5th Edition

SAMUEL A. BROVERMAN, PhD, ASA

ACTEX Publications

ISBN: 978-1-56698-768-4

CONTENTS

CHAPTER 6

CHAPTER 7

CHAPTER 8

CHAPTER 9

CHAPTER 1

1.1.1 Balances are $10,000(1.04) = 10,400$ after one year,

$10,000(1.04)^2 = 10,816$ after 2 years, and

$10,000(1.04)^3 = 11,248.64$ after 3 years.

Interest amounts are 400 at the end of the 1st year, 416 at the end of the 2nd year, and 432.64 at the end of the 3rd year.

1.1.2 (a) $2500[1 + (.04)(10)] = 3500$

(b) $2500(1.04)^{10} = 3700.61$

(c) $2500(1.02)^{20} = 3714.87$

(d) $2500(1.01)^{40} = 3722.16$

1.1.3 Balance after 12 months is $10,000(1.01)^3(1.0075)^9 = 11,019.70$. Average monthly interest rate is j, where

$10,000(1+j)^{12} = 11,019.70$.

Solving for j results in $.0081244$.

1.1.4   There are two (equivalent) ways to approach this problem. We can update the balance in the account at the time of each transaction until we reach the end of 10 years, and set the balance equal to 10,000 to solve for K:

Balance at $t = 4$ (after interest and withdrawal) is

$$10,000(1.04)^4 - (1.05)K;$$

balance at $t = 5$ is

$$\left[10,000(1.04)^4 - (1.05)K\right](1.04) - (1.05)K;$$

balance at $t = 6$ is

$$\left[\left[10,000(1.04)^4 - (1.05)K\right](1.04) - (1.05)K\right](1.04) - K;$$

at $t = 7$ is

$$\left[\left[\left[10,000(1.04)^4 - (1.05)K\right]\right.\right.$$

$$\left.\left.(1.04) - (1.05)K\right](1.04) - K\right](1.04) - K;$$

at $t = 10$ there is 3 years of compounding from time 7, so that

$$\left[\left[\left[10,000(1.04)^4 - (1.05)K\right](1.04) - (1.05)K\right]\right.$$

$$\left.(1.04) - K\right](1.04) - K\right](1.04)^3 = 10,000.$$

Solving for K from this equation results in $K = 979.93$.

Alternatively, we can accumulate to time 10 the initial deposit and the withdrawals separately. The balance at time 10 is

$$10,000(1.04)^{10} - K(1.05)(1.04)^6 - K(1.05)(1.04)^5$$

$$- K(1.04)^4 - K(1.04)^3 = 10,000.$$

This is the same equation as in the first approach (and must result in the same value of K). In general, when using compound interest, for a series of deposits and withdrawals that occur at various points in time, the balance in an account at any given time point is the accumulated values of all deposits minus the accumulated values of all withdrawals to that time point. This is also the idea behind the "dollar-weighted rate of return," which will be discussed later.

1.1.5   (a) Over 5 years the unit value has grown by a factor of $(1.10)(1.16)(1-.07)(1.04)(1.32) = 1.629074$. The average annual (compound) growth is $(1.629074)^{1/5} = 1.1025$, or average annual growth of 10.25% for 5 years.

      (b) Five-year average annual return from January 1, 1996 to December 31, 2005 is j, where $(1+j)^5(1.17)^5 = (1.13)^{10}$, so that $j = .0914$. Annual return for 2004 is k, where $(1+k)(1.22) = (1.15)^2$, so that $k = .084$.

      (c) Over n years the growth is $(1+i_1)(1+i_2)\cdots(1+i_n) = (1+i)^n$, where the average annual (compound) interest rate is i, so that $i+1$ is the geometric mean of $1+i_1, 1+i_2, \ldots, 1+i_n$.

Thus, $1+i \leq \dfrac{(1+i_1)+(1+i_2)+\cdots+(1+i_n)}{n} \to i \leq \dfrac{i_1+i_2+\cdots+i_n}{n}$.

1.1.6   We equate the accumulated value of Joe's deposits with that of Tina's. Note that it is assumed that for simple interest, each new deposit is considered separately and begins earning simple interest from the time of the new deposit.

$$10[1+10(.1)] + 30[1+5(.1)] = 67.5$$

$$= 10(1.0915)^{10-n} + 30(1.0915)^{10-2n}.$$

This can be solved by substituting in the possible values of n until the equation is satisfied. Alternatively, the equation can be rewritten as

$$67.5(1.0195)^{2n} - 10(1.0915)^{10}(1.0915)^n - 30(1.0915)^{10} = 0$$

which is a quadratic equation in $(1.0915)^n$. The solution is

$$(1.0915)^n = \frac{24 \pm 141.5}{135}.$$

We ignore the negative root and get $(1.0915)^n = 1.226 \to n = 2.3$.

1.1.7 (a) $1000 = 850\left[1+i\left(\frac{60}{365}\right)\right] \rightarrow i = 1.0735(107.35\%)$

(b) $1000 = 900\left[1+i\left(\frac{60}{365}\right)\right] \rightarrow i = .6759(67.59\%)$

(c) $900\left[1+(.09)\left(\frac{60}{365}\right)\right] = 913.32$

(d) $900\left[1+(.09)\left(\frac{d}{365}\right)\right] = 1000 \rightarrow d = 451$

1.1.8 It is to Smith's advantage to take the loan of 975 on the 7th day if the amount payable on the 30th day is less than the amount due to the supplier:

$$975\left[1+i\frac{23}{365}\right] \le 1000 \rightarrow i \le .4069.$$

1.1.9 (a) Maturity value of 180-day certificate is
$$100,000\left(1+.075\left(\frac{180}{365}\right)\right) = 103,698.63.$$

Interim book value after 120 days is
$$100,000\left(1+.075\left(\frac{120}{365}\right)\right) = 102,465.75.$$

Bank will pay X after 120 days so that
$$X\left(1+.09\left(\frac{60}{365}\right)\right) = 103,698.63 \rightarrow X = 102,186.82.$$
The penalty charged is $102,465.75 - 102,186.82 = 278.93$.

(b) $1.08 = \left(1+\frac{.075}{2}\right)\left(1+\frac{i}{2}\right) \rightarrow i = .0819$

1.1.10 (a) $1000(1.12)^t = 3000 \rightarrow t = \dfrac{\ln(3)}{\ln(1.12)} = 9.694$ (9 years and

approximately 253 days).

(b) At the end of 9 years the accumulated value is $1000(1.12)^9 = 2773.08$. At time s during the 10th year, the accumulated value based on simple interest within the 10th year is $2773.08(1+.12s)$. Setting this equal to 3000 and solving for s results in $s = \dfrac{\left(\frac{3000}{2773.08}\right) - 1}{.12} = .6819$ years (approximately 249 days) after the end of 9 years.

(c) $1000(1.01)^t = 3000 \rightarrow t = \dfrac{\ln(3)}{\ln(1.01)} = 110.41$ months (about 9 years and 2 months and 13 days).

(d) $1000(1+i)^{10} = 3000 \rightarrow i = 3^{1/10} - 1 = .1161$ (11.61% per year).

(e) $1000(1+j)^{120} = 3000 \rightarrow i = 3^{1/120} - 1 = .009197$ (.9197% per month).

1.1.11 (a) $(1.0075)^{67/17} = 1.0299 < 1.03$
$\left(\text{but } (1.0075)^{68/17} = (1.0075)^4 = 1.0303\right)$

(b) $(1.015)^{67/17} = 1.0604 > 1.06$

1.1.12 (a) Smith buys $\dfrac{910}{4} = 227.5$ units after the front-end load is paid. Six months later she receives $(227.5)(5)(.985) = 1120.4375$. Smith's 6-month rate of return is 12.04% on her initial 1000.

(b) If unit value had dropped to 3.50, she receives $(227.5)(3.5)(.985) = 784.30625$, which is a 6-month effective rate of -21.57%.

1.1.13   We use the following result from calculus: if f and g are differentiable functions such that $f(a) = g(a)$ and $f'(x) < g'(x)$ for $a < x < b$, then $f(b) < g(b)$.

(i)   Suppose $0 < t < 1$. Let $f(i) = (1+i)^t$ and $g(i) = 1 + i \cdot t$. Then $f(0) = g(0) = 1$. If we can show that $f'(i) < g'(i)$ for any $i > 0$, then we can use the calculus result above to conclude that $f(i) < g(i)$ for any $i > 0$. First note that $f'(i) = t \cdot (1+i)^{t-1}$ and $g'(i) = t$. Since $i > 0$, it follows that $1 + i > 1$, and since $t < 1$, it follows that $t - 1 < 0$. Then $(1+i)^{t-1} < 1$, so $f'(i) < g'(i)$.

This completes the proof of part (i).

(ii)   Suppose that $t > 1$. Let $f(i) = 1 + i \cdot t$ and $g(i) = (1+i)^t$. Again $f(0) = g(0)$. If we can show that $f'(i) < g'(i)$ for any $i > 0$, then we can use the calculus result above to conclude that $f(i) < g(i)$ for any $i > 0$. Since $t > 1$ and $i > 0$ it follows that $t - 1 > 0$ and $1 + i > 1$. Thus $(1+i)^{t-1} > 1$, and it follows that $f'(i) = t < t \cdot (1+i)^{t-1} = g'(i)$. This completes the proof of part (ii).

1.1.14   Original graph is $y = (1+i)^t$. New graph is $10^y = (1+i)^t$, or, equivalently, $y = t \cdot \dfrac{\ln(1+i)}{\ln(10)}$, so that y is now a linear function of t.

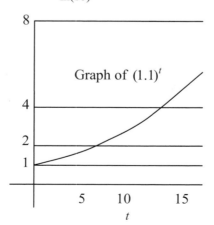

Graph of $(1.1)^t$

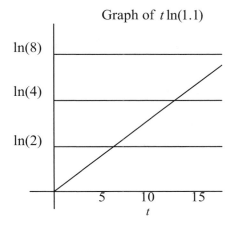

Graph of $t \ln(1.1)$

SECTIONS 1.2 AND 1.3

1.2.1   Present value is

$$5000\left[\frac{1}{1.06} + \frac{1}{(1.06)^2} + \frac{1}{(1.06)^3} + \frac{1}{(1.06)^4}\right] = 17,325.53.$$

1.2.2   Amount now required is

$$25,000[v^{17} + v^{15} + v^{12}] + 100,000[v^{20} + v^{18} + v^{15}] = 75,686$$

1.2.3 $28 = 15 + 16.50v \rightarrow v = .78779 \rightarrow i = .2692$

1.2.4 $1000 \cdot v_{.06}^3 \cdot v_{.07}^4 \cdot v_{.09}^3 = 494.62$

1.2.5   Equation of value on July 1, 2013 is

$$200(1.04) + 300v = 100(1.04)^4 + X \rightarrow X = 379.48.$$

1.2.6 $480 = 50 + 100(v + v^2 + v^3 + v^4) + Xv^5$, where $v = \frac{1}{1.03}$,

so that $X = 67.57$. If interest is .01 per month, then $v = \frac{1}{(1.01)^3}$

and $X = 67.98$.

1.2.7 $100 + 200v^n + 300v^{2n} = 600v^{10} \rightarrow$

$600v^{10} = 100 + 200(.75941) + 300(.75941)^2$

$\rightarrow v^{10} = .708155 \rightarrow i = (.708155)^{-.1} - 1 = .0351.$

1.2.8 (a) $(20)(2000)[v + v^2 + v^3 + \cdots + v^{48}] = 1,607,391$ (at .75%)

(b) $1,607,391 + 200,000v^{48} = 1,747,114$

(c) $X = 1,607,391 + .15Xv^{48} \rightarrow X = 1,795,551$

1.2.9 $750 = 367.85[1 + (1+j)] \rightarrow j = .0389$ is the 2-month rate.

1.2.10 With X initially stocked, the number after 4 years is

$X(1.4)^4 - 5000[(1.4)^{1.5} + (1.4)^{.5}] = X \rightarrow X = 4997.$

1.2.11 $1000 = \frac{100}{(1+j)^2} + \frac{1000}{(1+j)^3}$, and $1000 = \frac{100}{1+k} + \frac{1000}{(1+k)^3}$. It is not possible that $j = k$, since the two present values could not both be equal to 1000 (unless $j = k = 0$, which is not true). If $j > k$, then $(1+j)^2 > 1+k$ and $(1+j)^3 > (1+k)^3$, in which case the first present value would have to be less than the second present value. Since both present values are 1000, it must be the case that $j < k$ ($j = .0333$ and $k = .0345$).

1.2.12 $1000(1+i)^2 + 1092 = 2000(1+i)$

Solving the quadratic equation for $1+i$ results in no real roots.

1.2.13 (a) $\frac{d}{di}(1+i)^n = n(1+i)^{n-1}$ (c) $\frac{d}{dn}(1+i)^n = (1+i)^n \ln(1+i)$

     (b) $\frac{d}{di}v^n = -nv^{n+1}$ (d) $\frac{d}{dn}v^n = -v^n \ln(1+i)$

1.2.14 With an annual yield rate quoted to the nearest .01%, the annual yield i is in the interval $.11065 \le i < .11075$.

Since the quoted annual yield rate is $\frac{365}{182} \cdot \frac{100-\text{Price}}{\text{Price}}$ it follows that $.11065 \le \frac{365}{182} \cdot \frac{100-\text{Price}}{\text{Price}} < .11075$, or, equivalently, $94.767 \le$ Price < 94.771.

1.2.15 (a) $P = \dfrac{1000,000}{1+(.10)\frac{182}{365}} = 95,250.52$

     (b) $P = \dfrac{100,000}{1+i\cdot\frac{182}{365}} \rightarrow \dfrac{dP}{di} = -\dfrac{100,000}{\left(1+i\cdot\frac{182}{365}\right)^2} \cdot \dfrac{182}{365}$

         $= -45,239.03$ if $i = .10$

         $\dfrac{dP}{di} \doteq \dfrac{\Delta P}{\Delta i} \doteq -45,239.03 \rightarrow \Delta P \doteq -45.239.03 \cdot \Delta i.$

         If $\Delta i = .001$, then $\Delta P \doteq -45.24$.

     (c) $P = \dfrac{100,000}{1+i\cdot\frac{91}{265}} \rightarrow \dfrac{dP}{di} = -\dfrac{100,000}{\left(1+i\cdot\frac{91}{265}\right)^2} \cdot \dfrac{91}{365} = -23,733.34$ if $i = .10$.

         As the T-bill approaches its due date the $\frac{dP}{di}$ goes to 0.

1.2.16 (a) $B_1 = B_0(1+i) + \sum\limits_{k=1}^{n} a_k \left[1 + i(1-t_k)\right]$

$= B_0 + \sum\limits_{k=1}^{n} a_k + \left[B_0 + \sum\limits_{k=1}^{n} a_k(1-t_k) \right] \cdot i$

(b) The balance is B_0 for t_1 years, $B_0 + a_1$ for $t_2 - t_1$ years, $B_0 + a_1 + a_2$ for $t_3 - t_2$ years, $B_0 + a_1 + a_2 + \cdots + a_n$ for $1 - t_n$ years. The average balance is

$$\bar{B} = \frac{B_0 t_1 + (B_0 + a_1)(t_2 - t_1) + (B_0 + a_1 + a_2)(t_3 - t_2) + \cdots + (B_0 + a_1 + a_2 + \cdots + a_n)(1 - t_n)}{t_1 + (t_2 - t_1) - (t_3 - t_2) + \cdots + (1 - t_n)}$$

$$= B_0 + a_1(1 - t_1) + a_2(1 - t_2) + \cdots + a_n(1 - t_n)$$

$$= B_0 + \sum\limits_{k=1}^{n} a_k(1 - t_k).$$

(c) Follows directly from (a) and (b).

1.2.17 The difference between the two payment plans is that the first 2 payments are deferred for 2 months, so the saving is

$$30\left[(1+v) - (v^{24} + v^{25})\right] = 12.68.$$

Alternatively, the present value under the current payment plan is

$$30[1 + v + v^2 + \cdots + v^{23}] = 643.67.$$

The present value under Smith's proposed payment plan is

$$30[v^2 + \cdots + v^{25}] = 643.67v^2 = 630.99.$$

Saving is 12.68.

1.2.18 (a) Minimum monthly balance for January 2005 is 2500, for February 2005 is 6000, and for March 2005 is 9500. Interest earned is $(.10)\left(\frac{1}{12}\right)[2500 + 6000 + 9500] = 150$.

Balance on March 31 is $2500(4) + 1000(3) + 150 = 13,150$.

(b) Minimum daily balance is 2500 for January 1-15, 3500 for January 16-31, 6000 for February 1-15, 7000 for February 16-28, 9500 for March 1-15, and 10,500 for March 16-31. Interest earned is

$$(.10)\left(\frac{1}{365}\right)((2500(15) + 3500(16) + 6000(15) + 7000(13)$$
$$+ 9500(15) + 10,500(16)) = 160.27.$$

Balance on March 31 is

$$2500(4) + 1000(3) + 160.27 = 13,160.27.$$

(c) Minimum monthly balance for January 2005 is 2500, so interest on January 31 is $\frac{10}{12}(2500) = 20.83$, so balance on January 31 (after deposit and interest) is 6020.83.

Minimum monthly balance for February 2005 is 6020.83, so interest on February 28 is $\frac{10}{12}(6020.83) = 50.17$, so balance on February 28 is 9571.00.

Minimum monthly balance for March 2005 is 9571, so interest on March 31 is $\frac{10}{12}(9571) = 79.76$, so balance on March 31 is 13,150.76.

(d) Minimum daily balance is 2500 for January 1-15 and 3500 for January 16-31, so interest on January 31 is 25.62.

Minimum daily balance is 6025.62 for February 1-15 and 7025.62 for February 16-28, so interest on February 28 is 49.79.

Minimum daily balance is 9575.41 for March 1-15 and 10,575.41 for March 16-31, so interest on March 31 is 85.71.

Balance on March 31 is 13,161.12.

SECTION 1.4

1.4.1 $m = 1$ implies interest convertible annually ($m=1$ time per year), which implies the effective annual interest rate $i^{(1)} = i = .12$. We use Equation (1.5) to solve for i for the other values of m, as shown below.

m (Effective Period)	$\frac{1}{m}$-year effective interest rate $\frac{i^{(m)}}{m}$	$i = \left[1 + \frac{i^{(m)}}{m}\right]^m - 1$
1 (1 year)	$\frac{i^{(1)}}{1} = \frac{.12}{1} = .12$	$(1.12)^1 - 1 = .12$
2 (6 months)	$\frac{i^{(2)}}{2} = \frac{.12}{2} = .06$	$(1.06)^2 - 1 = .1236$
3 (4 months)	$\frac{i^{(3)}}{3} = \frac{.12}{3} = .04$	$(1.04)^3 - 1 = .124864$
4 (3 months)	$\frac{i^{(4)}}{4} = \frac{.12}{4} = .03$	$(1.03)^4 - 1 = .125509$
6 (2 months)	$\frac{i^{(6)}}{6} = \frac{.12}{6} = .02$	$(1.02)^6 - 1 = .126162$
8 (1.5 months)	$\frac{i^{(8)}}{8} = \frac{.12}{8} = .015$	$(1.015)^8 - 1 = .126593$
12 (1 months)	$\frac{i^{(12)}}{12} = \frac{.12}{12} = .01$	$(1.01)^{12} - 1 = .126825$
52 (1 week)	$\frac{i^{(52)}}{52} = \frac{.12}{52} = .0023$	$\left(1 + \frac{.12}{365}\right)^{52} - 1 = .127341$
365 (1 day)	$\frac{i^{(365)}}{365} = \frac{.12}{365} = .00033$	$\left(1 + \frac{.12}{365}\right)^{365} - 1 = .127475$
∞	$\lim_{y \to \infty}\left(1 + \frac{.12}{y}\right)^y - 1 = e^{.12} - 1 = .127497$	

1.4.2 (a) $1000v_{.045}^{20} = 414.64$

(b) $1000v_{.015}^{60} = 409.30$

(c) $1000v_{.0075}^{120} = 407.94$

1.4.3   Equivalent effective annual rates are
Mountain Bank: $(1.075)^2 - 1 = .155625$
River Bank:

$$\left(1 + \frac{i^{(365)}}{365}\right)^{365} - 1 \geq .155625$$

$$\rightarrow \left(1 + \frac{i^{(365)}}{365}\right)^{365} \geq (1.155625)^{1/365} = 1.000396356$$

$$\rightarrow i^{(365)} \geq .144670$$

1.4.4   The last 6 months of the 8th year is the time from the end of the 15th to the end of the 16th half-year.

$$0 \quad 1H \quad 2H=1Y \qquad 3H \quad 4H=2Y \text{ --- } 14H=7Y \quad 15H \quad 16H=8Y$$

The amount of interest earned in Eric's account in the 16th half-year is the change in balance from time $15H$ to time $16H$.

The balances at those points are $X\left(1 + \frac{i}{2}\right)^{15}$ and $X\left(1 + \frac{i}{2}\right)^{16}$. The amount of interest earned by Eric in the period is

$$X\left(1 + \frac{i}{2}\right)^{16} - X\left(1 + \frac{i}{2}\right)^{15} = X\left(1 + \frac{i}{2}\right)^{15}\left(\frac{i}{2}\right).$$

The balance in Mike's account at the end of the 15th half-year (7.5 years) is $2X(1+7.5i)$, and the balance at the end of the 16th half-year (8 years) is $2X(1+8i)$.

The interest earned by Mike in that period is

$$2X(1+8i) - 2X(1+7.5i) = 2X(.5i) = 2X\left(\frac{i}{2}\right).$$

We are told that Eric and Mike earn the same amount of interest. Therefore, $X\left(1 + \frac{i}{2}\right)^{15}\left(\frac{i}{2}\right) = 2X\left(\frac{i}{2}\right)$, so that $\left(1 + \frac{i}{2}\right)^{15} = 2$. Then $i = 2[2^{1/15} - 1] = .0946$.

1.4.5　Quarterly effective rate is $\frac{.0325}{4} = .008125$. Initial amount invested after commission is .99. At the end of 3 months, the accumulated value is $.99(1.008125)$. This is then subject to the 1% commission for the rollover and then the 3-month interest rate of .008125. At the end of the year, the accumulated value is $[.99(1.008125)]^4 = .992198 = 1 - .0078$. The effective after-commission return is $-.78\%$.

1.4.6　$i^{(.5)} = .5[(1.10)^{1/.5} - 1] = .105$

$i^{(.25)} = .25[(1.1)^{1/.25} - 1] = .116025$

$i^{(.1)} = .10[(1.10)^{1/.1} - 1] = .159374$

$i^{(.01)} = .01[(1.10)^{1/.01} - 1] = 137.796$

1.4.7　From November 9 to January 1 (53 days) Smith earns (two full months) interest of $\frac{2}{12}(.1125)(1000) = 18.75$. Thus, Smith earns a 53-day effective rate of interest of .01875. The equivalent effective annual rate of interest is $i = (1.01875)^{365/53} - 1 = .1365$.

1.4.8　Left on deposit for a year at $i^{(12)} = .09$, X accumulates to $X(1.0075)^{12}$. If the monthly interest is reinvested at monthly rate .75%, the accumulated value at the end of the year is

$$X + X(.0075)\left[(1.0075)^{11} + (1.0075)^{10} + \cdots + (1.0075) + 1\right].$$

Since $1 + r + r^2 + \cdots + r^k = \frac{r^{k+1} - 1}{r - 1}$, it follows that the total at the end of the year with reinvestment of interest is

$$X\left[1 + (.0075) \cdot \frac{(1.0075)^{12} - 1}{1.0075 - 1}\right] = X(1.0075)^{12}.$$

1.4.9 (a) We wish to show that

$$f'(m) = f(m) \cdot \left[\ln\left(1 + \frac{j}{m}\right) - \frac{\frac{j}{m}}{1 + \frac{j}{m}} \right] > 0. \text{ First, } f(m) > 0,$$

since $j > 0$. Also, if $x > 0$ and $h(x) = \ln(1+x) - \frac{x}{1+x}$, then

$h'(x) = \frac{x}{(1+x)^2} > 0$, and since $h(0) = 0$, it follows that

$h(x) > 0$ for all $x > 0$. Letting $x = \frac{j}{m} > 0$, we see that

$\ln\left(1 + \frac{j}{m}\right) - \frac{\frac{j}{m}}{1 + \frac{j}{m}} > 0$, which implies that $f'(m) > 0$.

(b) $g'(m) = (1+j)^{1/m} - 1 - \frac{(1+j)^{1/m} \cdot \ln(1+j)}{m}$

$$= (1+j)^{1/m} \cdot \left[(1 - \ln(1+j)^{1/m}) \right] - 1.$$

But $x[1 - \ln x]$ has a maximum of 1 at $x = 1$, so that with

$(1+j)^{1/m} = x$, we see that $g'(m) < 0$ for $m > 1$.

(c) Consider $\ln[f(m)] = m \cdot \ln\left(1 + \frac{j}{m}\right) = \frac{\ln\left(1 + \frac{j}{m}\right)}{\frac{1}{m}}$. Then

$$\lim_{m \to \infty} \ln[f(m)] = \lim_{m \to \infty} \frac{\ln\left(1 + \frac{j}{m}\right)}{\frac{1}{m}} = \lim_{m \to \infty} \frac{\frac{1}{1 + (j/m)} \cdot \left(-\frac{j}{m^2}\right)}{-\frac{1}{m^2}} = j.$$

Thus $\lim_{m \to \infty} f(m) = e^j$.

(d) $g(m) = \frac{(1+j)^{1/m} - 1}{\frac{1}{m}}, \quad \lim_{m \to \infty} g(m) = \lim_{m \to \infty} \frac{(1+j)^{1/m} \cdot \left(-\frac{\ln(1+j)}{m^2}\right)}{-\frac{1}{m^2}}$

$= \ln(1+j)$, since $\lim_{m \to \infty} (1+j)^{1/m} = 1$.

1.4.10 We want to find the smallest integer m so that

$$f(m) = \left[1 + \frac{.17}{m}\right]^m \geq 1.18, \ f(2) = 1.1772, \ f(3) = 1.1798,$$

$f(4) = 1.1811 \to m = 4$.

With 16%, we see that $\lim_{m \to \infty} \left[1 + \frac{.16}{m}\right]^m = e^{.16} = 1.1735$, so that

no matter how many times per year compounding takes place, a nominal rate of interest of 16% cannot accumulate to an effective rate of more than 17.35%.

SECTION 1.5

1.5.1 (a) $4992 = \dfrac{X}{(1.08)^{1/2}} \rightarrow X = 5187.84$

(b) $4992 = \dfrac{X}{\left[1+(.08)\left(\frac{1}{2}\right)\right]} \rightarrow X = 5191.68$

(c) $4992 = X(1-.08)^{1/2} \rightarrow X = 5204.52$

(d) $4992 = X\left[1-(.08)\left(\frac{1}{2}\right)\right] \rightarrow X = 5200$

1.5.2 With a quoted discount rate of .940, the price of a 91-day T-Bill should be $100(1-\dfrac{91}{360}\times.0113) = 99.714$ as quoted.

The investment rate is found as $\left(\dfrac{100}{99.714}-1\right)\times\dfrac{365}{91} = .0115$, as quoted.

1.5.3 $d_j = \dfrac{A(r+T)-A(r)}{A(r+T)} = 1-\dfrac{A(r)}{A(r+T)}$, and

$j = \dfrac{A(r+T)-A(r)}{A(r)} = \dfrac{A(r+T)}{A(r)}-1$

$\rightarrow 1-d_j = \dfrac{A(r)}{A(r+T)} = \dfrac{1}{1+j} \rightarrow$

(a) $d_j = \dfrac{j}{1+j}$ and (b) $j = \dfrac{d_j}{1-d_j}$.

1.5.4 $1.15 = (1-d)(1.3) \rightarrow d = .1154$

1.5.5 Bruce's interest in year 11: $100(1-d)^{-10}\cdot\left[(1-d)^{-1}-1\right] = X.$
Robbie's interest in year 17:

$50(1-d)^{-16}\cdot\left[(1-d)^{-1}-1\right] = X = 100(1-d)^{-10}\cdot\left[(1-d)^{-1}-1\right]$
$\rightarrow 50(1-d)^{-16} = 100(1-d)^{-10} \rightarrow (1-d)^6 = .5 \rightarrow d = .1091$
$\rightarrow X = 38.9$

1.5.6 The present value of 1 due in n years is $(1-d)^n$, so the accumulated value after n years of an initial investment of 1 is

$$\frac{1}{(1-d)^n} = (1-d)^{-n}.$$

1.5.7 The initial deposit of 10 grows to $10\left(1-\frac{d}{4}\right)^{-40}$ at the end of 10 years (40 quarters), and then continues to grow at 3% per half year after that. The accumulated value of the initial deposit of 10 at the end of 30 years is $10\left(1-\frac{d}{4}\right)^{-40} \times (1.03)^{40}$ (20 more years, 40 more half-years at 3% per half-year).

The second deposit is 20 made at time 15. The accumulated value of the second deposit at time 30 (15 years after the second deposit) is $20(1.03)^{30}$ (15 years is 30 half-years).

The total accumulated value at the end of 30 years is

$$10\left(1-\frac{d}{4}\right)^{-40} \times (1.03)^{40} + 20(1.03)^{30} = 100.$$

Solving for d results in $d = .0453$.

This question is from the May 2003 Course 2 exam that was conducted jointly by the Society of Actuaries and the Casualty Actuarial Society. It should be noted that the nominal interest rate notation $i^{(m)}$ and nominal discount rate notation $d^{(m)}$ is not always specifically used on the professional actuarial exams. In this example, the notation d was a nominal annual rate of discount compounded quarterly.

1.5.8 (a) Bank pays

$$1 - d \cdot \frac{n}{365} = \frac{1}{1+i\cdot\frac{n}{365}} \rightarrow i = \frac{365}{n}\left[\frac{1}{1-d\cdot\frac{n}{365}} - 1\right] = \frac{d}{1-d\cdot\frac{n}{365}}.$$

As n increases, i increases.

(b) From (a) $1 - dt = \frac{1}{1+it} \rightarrow d = \frac{i}{1+it}$. If $i = .11$ then

$t = 1 \rightarrow d = .099099$, $t = .50 \rightarrow d = .104265$,

$t = \frac{1}{12} \rightarrow d = .109001$.

1.5.9 Suppose that the T-Bill's face amount is $100. Then Smith purchases the bill for $100\left[1 - \frac{182}{360}(.10)\right] = 94.94$ (nearest .01). 91 days later, the value of the T-Bill is

$$100\left[1 - \frac{91}{360}(.10)\right] = 97.47.$$

Smith's return for the 91 days is $\frac{97.47}{94.94} - 1 = .0266$ (2.66%).

1.5.10 From Exercise 1.5.3, we have $\frac{d^{(m)}}{m} = d_j$, and $\frac{i^{(m)}}{m} = j$, so

(a) $\frac{d^{(m)}}{m} = d_j = \frac{j}{1+j} = \frac{\frac{i^{(m)}}{m}}{1 + \frac{i^{(m)}}{m}} \rightarrow d^{(m)} = \frac{i^{(m)}}{1 + \frac{i^{(m)}}{m}}$, and

(b) $i^{(m)} = \frac{d^{(m)}}{1 - \frac{d^{(m)}}{m}}$.

1.5.11 $1000 = 1200\left(\frac{1}{1+i}\right)(1-i) \rightarrow i = .0909$

1.5.12 $1000(1+j) = 1000 + 40(1+j)^2 \rightarrow (1+j)^2 - 25(1+j) + 25 = 0$
        $\rightarrow 1+j = 1.043561$ or 23.9564. Since $j < .10$, it follows that
        $j = .0436$.

SECTION 1.6

1.6.1 Accumulated value at time 1 is

$$10,000 \times e^{\int_0^1 .05\,dt} = 10,000 \times e^{.05} = 10,512.71.$$

Accumulated value at time 2 is

$$10,000 \times e^{\int_0^1 .05\,dt + \int_1^2 [.05 + .02(t-1)]\,dt} = 10,000 \times e^{.05 + .06} = 11,162.78$$

1.6.2 $\left(1+\frac{i^{(4)}}{4}\right)^{16} = e^{\int_0^3 .02t\,dt + \int_3^4 .045\,dt} = e^{.09+.045} \rightarrow i^{(4)} = .0339.$

1.6.3 $\exp(\int_0^5 \frac{t^2}{k}\,dt) = (1-.04)^{-10} \rightarrow e^{125/3k} = 1.50414$

$\rightarrow \frac{125}{3k} = \ln(1.50414) \rightarrow k = 102.$

1.6.4 Effective annual rate for Tawny is $i = (1.05)^2 - 1 = .1025.$
Tawny: $\delta = \ln(1.1025) = .09758.$

Fabio: Simple interest rate $j \rightarrow \delta_t = \frac{j}{1+tj}.$

At time 5,
$.09758 = \frac{j}{1+5j} \rightarrow j = .1906 \rightarrow Z = 1000[1+5j] = 1953.$

1.6.5 $100\left[e^{\int_0^6 .01t^2\,dt} - e^{\int_0^3 .01t^2\,dt}\right] + X\left[e^{\int_3^6 .01t^2\,dt} - 1\right] = X$

$\rightarrow 100(e^{.72} - e^{.09}) = X(2 - e^{.63}) \rightarrow X = 784.6.$

1.6.6 Bruce's 6-month rate of interest is $\frac{i}{2}$, and 7.25 years is 14.5 6-month periods. Bruce's accumulated value after 7.25 years is
$100\left(1+\frac{i}{2}\right)^{14.5} = 200.$ Solving for i, we get

$$\left(1+\frac{i}{2}\right) = 2^{1/14.5} \rightarrow i = .0979.$$

Peter's account grows to $100e^{7.25\delta} = 200$, so that
$\delta = \frac{1}{7.25}\ln 2 = .0956.$ Then $i - \delta = .0023 = .23\%.$

1.6.7 $e^\delta \cdot (e^{1.5\delta})^4 = 1.36086 \rightarrow e^{7\delta} = 1.36086 \rightarrow 1+i = e^\delta = 1.045$

1.6.8 (a) $(1+i)^5 = \exp\left[\int_0^5 \left(.08 + \frac{.025t}{t+1}\right) dt\right] = 1.616407 \rightarrow i = .1008$

(b) $1+i_1 = \exp\left[\int_0^1 \left(.08 + \frac{.025t}{t+1}\right) dt\right] = 1.091629 \rightarrow i_1 = .091629$

$1+i_2 = \exp\left[\int_1^2 \left(.08 + \frac{.025t}{t+1}\right) dt\right] = 1.099509 \rightarrow i_2 = .099509$

$i_3 = .102751, \quad i_4 = .104532, \quad i_5 = .105659$

(c) $1000 \cdot \exp\left[-\int_2^4 \left(.08 + \frac{.025t}{t+1}\right) dt\right] = 821.00$

1.6.9 $Ke^{-2\delta} = 960, \ Ke^{-\delta} = 1200 \rightarrow e^{-\delta} = 1 - d = .80 \rightarrow K = 1500$
and $d = .20$. If d changes to $.10$, then the present value becomes
$1500(1-.10)^2 = 1215$.

1.6.10 $i = e^\delta - 1, \ \delta' = 2\delta \rightarrow$

$i' = e^{\delta'} - 1 = e^{2\delta} - 1 = (1+i)^2 - 1 = 2i + i^2 > 2i,$

$d' = 1 - e^{\delta'} = 1 - e^{-2\delta} = 1 - (1-d)^2 = 2d - d^2 < 2d$

1.6.11 (a) $1000(1.02)^2 \left[1 + (.08)\left(\frac{19}{365}\right)\right] = 1044.73$

(b) For $0 < t \le \frac{1}{4}, \ A(t) = 1000[1 + (.08)t]$

for $\frac{1}{4} \le t \le \frac{1}{2}, \ A(t) = 1000(1.02)\left[1 + (.08)\left(t - \frac{1}{4}\right)\right]$

for $\frac{1}{2} \le t \le \frac{3}{4}, \ A(t) = 1000(1.02)^2\left[1 + (.08)\left(t - \frac{1}{2}\right)\right]$

for $\frac{3}{4} \le t \le 1, \ A(t) = 1000(1.02)^3\left[1 + (.08)\left(t - \frac{3}{4}\right)\right]$

(c) For $0 < t = \frac{1}{4}$, $\delta_t = \frac{S'(t)}{S(t)} = \frac{.08}{1+(.08)t}$.

To find $\delta_{t+1/4}$, let $r = t + \frac{1}{4}$, or $t = r - \frac{1}{4}$.

Then

$$\delta_{t+1/4,} = \delta_r = \frac{S'\left(t+\frac{1}{4}\right)}{S\left(t+\frac{1}{4}\right)}$$

$$= \frac{S'(r)}{S(r)} = \frac{1000(1.02)(.08)}{1000(1.02)\left[1+(.08)\left(r-\frac{1}{4}\right)\right]} = \frac{.08}{1+(.08)t}.$$

The same occurs for $t + \frac{1}{2}$ and $t + \frac{3}{4}$.

1.6.12 (a) $\dfrac{A\left(t+\frac{1}{m}\right)-A(t)}{A\left(t+\frac{1}{m}\right)}$

(b) $d^{(m)} = m \cdot \dfrac{A\left(t+\frac{1}{m}\right)-A(t)}{A\left(t+\frac{1}{m}\right)} = \dfrac{A\left(t+\frac{1}{m}\right)-A(t)}{\frac{1}{m}\cdot A\left(t+\frac{1}{m}\right)}$

(c) Let $h = \frac{1}{m}$. Then $\displaystyle\lim_{m\to\infty} d^{(m)} = \lim_{h\to 0} \frac{A(t+h)-A(t)}{h\cdot A(t+h)} = \frac{A'(t)}{A(t)}$.

1.6.13 (a) $\delta_t = \dfrac{A'(t)}{A(t)} = \dfrac{a_1+2a_2t+\cdots+na_nt^{n-1}}{a_0+a_1t+\cdots+a_nt^n} \to \displaystyle\lim_{t\to\infty}\delta_t = 0$

(apply l'Hospital's rule)

(b) $A(t) = \exp\left[\displaystyle\int_0^t \delta_s\, ds\right] = \exp[k\cdot 2\cdot t^{1/2}]$.

$$\lim_{t\to\infty}\frac{A(t)}{1+it} = \lim_{t\to\infty}\frac{e^{2kt^{1/2}}\cdot\frac{k}{t^{1/2}}}{i} = \infty$$

$$\lim_{t\to\infty}\frac{A(t)}{(1+i)^t} = \lim_{t\to\infty}\frac{e^{2kt^{1/2}}\cdot\frac{k}{t^{1/2}}}{(1+i)^t\cdot\ln(1+i)}$$

$$= \lim_{t\to\infty}\frac{1}{t^{1/2}\ln(1+i)}\cdot\frac{1}{\exp\left[t\cdot\ln(1+i)-2kt^{1/2}\right]} = 0$$

SECTION 1.7

1.7.1 $i_{real} = \frac{i-r}{1+r} = \frac{.10-.15}{1+.15} = -.043478$

1.7.2   After-tax return is $\frac{(.12)(.55)-.10}{1.10} = -.0309.$

1.7.3   (a)   Smith's ATI this year will be

$$21,000(.75)+21,000(.50) = 26,250$$

and taxes paid will be 15,750. The real growth from last year to this year in Smith's ATI is $\frac{26,250/25,000}{1.05} = 1.00,$ and the real growth in taxes paid is $\frac{25,250/15,000}{1.05} = 1.00.$

       (b)   Continuing the old taxation scheme, Smith's taxes paid this year will be $(.25)(20,000)+(.50)(22,000) = 16,000,$ and his ATI will be 26,000. The real growth in taxes paid will be $\frac{16,000/15,000}{1.05} = 1.015873\,(1.59\%)$ and the real growth in ATI is $\frac{26,000/25,000}{1.05} = .990476 = 1-.009524(-.95\%).$

1.7.4   Smith sells the items for $100,000 \times 1.15 = 115,000$ at the end of the year and must pay back $100,000 \times 1.10 = 110,000.$ Net gain is 5,000 (in year-end dollars).

1.7.5 $e^{\delta_{real}} = 1+i_{real} = \frac{1+i}{1+r} = \frac{e^{\delta}}{e^{\delta_r}} = e^{\delta-\delta_r}$

1.7.6 $\frac{.18-.14}{1.14} = \frac{i-1}{2} \rightarrow i = 1.070175\,(107\%)$

1.7.7 Smith needs $\frac{1000}{1.09} = 917.4312$ US now if he invests in the US account. This is equivalent to $\frac{917.4312}{.73} = 1256.7551$ Cdn., which grows to 1382.4306 in one year in a Canadian dollar account earning 10%. The implication is that one year from now, 1000 US $\equiv$ 1382.4306 Cdn., or, equivalently, .723364 US $\equiv$ 1 Cdn.

1.7.8 $(1+r)^n \cdot v^n = \left(\frac{1+r}{1+i}\right)^n = \frac{1}{\left(\frac{1+i}{1+r}\right)^n} = \frac{1}{(1+i')^n}$

$\rightarrow 1+i' = \frac{1+i}{1+r} \rightarrow i' = \frac{i-r}{1+r}$

1.7.9 (a) Real after-tax rate of return on standard term deposit is $\frac{i(1-t_x)-r}{1+r}$, and on the indexed term deposit is

$$\frac{r+i'(1+r)(1-t_x)-r}{1+r} = i'(1-t_x).$$

(b) Setting the two expressions in part (a) equal and solving for i, we have $i = i'(1+r) + \frac{r}{1-t_x}$.

If $i' = .02$ and $r = .12$, then $i =$ (i) .1424, (ii) .1824, (iii) .2224, (iv) .3224.

CHAPTER 2

2.1.1   Option 1 accumulated value is $50,000(1+i)^{24}$.

Option 2 annuity payment is K, where $K = \dfrac{50,000}{a_{\overline{24}|.1}} = 5564.99$

Then $5564.99 s_{\overline{24}|.05} = 50,000(1+i)^{24}$ so that $i = 6.9\%$.

2.1.2   Suppose the annual effective rate is i. Then $900 s_{\overline{10}|i} = 1000 a_{\overline{\infty}|i}$

so that $900 \left[\dfrac{(1+i)^{10} - 1}{i} \right] = 1000 \left[\dfrac{1}{i} \right]$. and then $(1+i)^{10} = \dfrac{19}{9}$.

We then have $K s_{\overline{5}|i} \times (1+i)^5 = 1000 a_{\overline{\infty}|i}$ so that

$$K = \frac{1000}{(1+i)^{10} - (1+i)^5} = 1519.42.$$

2.1.3
$$
\begin{aligned}
s_{\overline{n+k}|i} &= \left[(1+i)^{n+k-1} + (1+i)^{n+k-2} + \cdots + (1+i)^{k+1} + (1+i)^k \right] \\
&\quad + \left[(1+i)^{k-1} + (1+i)^{k-2} + \cdots + (1+i) + 1 \right] \\
&= (1+i)^k \left[(1+i)^{n-1} + (1+i)^{n-2} + \cdots + (1+i)^1 + 1 \right] + s_{\overline{k}|i} \\
&= (1+i)^k \cdot s_{\overline{n}|i} + s_{\overline{k}|i}
\end{aligned}
$$

2.1.4
$$
\begin{aligned}
1000 s_{\overline{300}|.01} &= Y a_{\overline{300}|.01} \;\;\rightarrow\;\; Y = \frac{1000 s_{\overline{300}|.01}}{a_{\overline{300}|.01}} \\
&= 1000(1.01)^{300} = 19,788.47
\end{aligned}
$$

2.1.5   (i) $100 s_{\overline{7}|.0075} = 715.95$

(ii) $100 s_{\overline{19}|.0075} = 2033.87$

(iii) $100 \left[s_{\overline{19}|.0075} \cdot (1.00875)^9 (1.01)^4 + s_{\overline{9}|.00875} \cdot (1.01)^4 + s_{\overline{4}|.01} \right]$
$$= 3665.12$$

(iv) $3665.12(.01) = 36.65$

2.1.6 $98 s_{\overline{n}|}(1+i)^{2n} + 196 s_{\overline{2n}|} = 8000, \quad (1+i)^n = 2$

$\rightarrow 196 \left[2 s_{\overline{n}|} + s_{\overline{2n}|} \right] = 8000 \rightarrow 2 s_{\overline{n}|} + s_{\overline{2n}|} = 40.82$

$\rightarrow \dfrac{2(1+i)^n - 2}{i} + \dfrac{(1+i)^{2n} - 1}{i} = 40.82$

$\rightarrow \dfrac{2}{i} + \dfrac{3}{i} = 40.82 \rightarrow i = .1225.$

2.1.7   (a) $10(1.05)^{30} \cdot s_{\overline{10}|.05} + 20(1.05)^{20} \cdot s_{\overline{10}|.05}$
$$+ 30(1.05)^{10} \cdot s_{\overline{10}|.05} + 40 s_{\overline{10}|.05} = 2328.82$$

(b) $10 \left[s_{\overline{40}|} - s_{\overline{30}|} + 2(s_{\overline{30}|} - s_{\overline{20}|}) + 3(s_{\overline{20}|} - s_{\overline{10}|}) + 4 s_{\overline{10}|} \right]$
$$= 0 \left[s_{\overline{10}|.05} + s_{\overline{20}|.05} + s_{\overline{30}|.05} + s_{\overline{40}|.05} \right]$$

2.1.8 $\displaystyle\sum_{t=1}^{10} s_{\overline{t}|.10} = \sum_{t=1}^{10} \dfrac{(1.10)^t - 1}{.10} = 10 \left[\ddot{s}_{\overline{10}|.10} - 10 \right] = 11S - 100$

2.1.9 $I_t = i \cdot s_{\overline{t-1}|i} = (1+i)^{t-1} - 1 \rightarrow \displaystyle\sum_{t=1}^{n} I_t$
$$= \sum_{t=1}^{n} \left[(1+i)^{t-1} - 1 \right] = s_{\overline{n}|i} - n$$

Total interest = total accumulated value − total deposit

2.1.10 After n years Smith's AV is $\left[80s_{\overline{10}|.06} + 200\right](1.06)^{n-10}$ and

Brown's AV is $40s_{\overline{n-10}|.06} + P$. Thus, if $n = 15$, then $P = 14.53$,

$n = 20 \rightarrow P = 17.19$, $n = 25 \rightarrow 20.75$.

2.1.11 (a) $\dfrac{s_{\overline{2n}|i}}{s_{\overline{n}|i}} = \dfrac{(1+i)^{2n}-1}{(1+i)^n-1} = (1+i)^n +1 = \dfrac{210}{70} = 3$

$\rightarrow (1+i)^n = 2, \; 70 = s_{\overline{n}|i} = \dfrac{(1+i)^n -1}{i}$

$\rightarrow i = \dfrac{1}{70} = .014286, \; s_{\overline{3n}|i} = s_{\overline{n}|i} + (1+i)^n s_{\overline{2n}|i} = 490$

(b) $\dfrac{s_{\overline{3n}|i}}{s_{\overline{n}|i}} = \dfrac{(1+i)^{3n}-1}{(1+i)^n-1} = (1+i)^{2n} + (1+i)^n +1 = \dfrac{X}{Y}$

$\rightarrow$ quadratic equation in $z = (1+i)^n : z^2 + z + \dfrac{Y-X}{Y} = 0$

$\rightarrow (1+i)^n = z = \dfrac{-1 \pm \sqrt{1 - \frac{4(Y-X)}{Y}}}{2}$ (discard negative root)

$\rightarrow v^n = \dfrac{1}{(1+i)^n} = \dfrac{2}{-1+\sqrt{1-\frac{4(Y-X)}{Y}}}$

(c) $s_{\overline{n}|i} = (1+i)^2 \cdot s_{\overline{n-2}|i} + (1+i) + 1$

$\rightarrow 36.34(1+i)^2 + (1+i) - 47.99 = 0$

$\rightarrow 1+i = 1.1355,$ or -1.1630 (discard negative root)

2.1.12 $AV = s_{\overline{n}|.11} + (1.11)^n s_{\overline{m}|.07} = 128 + (1.11)^n (34)$

Since $s_{\overline{n}|.11} = \dfrac{(1.11)^n -1}{.11} = 128$, it follows that $(1.11)^n = 15.08$

$\rightarrow AV = 640.72$

2.1.13 We accumulate the payments to the beginning of the 6th year (time 5) and then accumulate them for another 5 years.

$20s_{\overline{6}|.1}(1.1)^5 + Xs_{\overline{3}|.1}(1.1)^5 = 200(1.04)^{10} \rightarrow X = 8.92$

2.1.14 An investment of amount 1 is equal to the present value of the return of principal in n years plus the present value of the interest generated over the n years.

2.1.15 2825.49

2.1.16 The equivalent effective annual rate of interest is
$i = (1.04)^2 - 1 = .0816$. The balance on January 1, 2010 is

$100,000(1.04)^{20} + 5000s_{\overline{10}|i} - 12,000s_{\overline{10}|i}(1.04) = 109,926$.

2.1.17 Annuity (a) has present value $55a_{\overline{20}|i}$.

The present value of annuity (b) can be formulated as $30a_{\overline{10}|i} + 60v^{10}a_{\overline{10}|i} + 90v^{20}a_{\overline{10}|i}$. Note that annuity (a) can also be written as $55a_{\overline{20}|i} = 55a_{\overline{10}|i} + 55v^{10}a_{\overline{10}|i}$. Both annuities have the same present value X, so that

$$55a_{\overline{10}|i} + 55v^{10}a_{\overline{10}|i} = 30a_{\overline{10}|i} + 60v^{10}a_{\overline{10}|i} + 90v^{20}a_{\overline{10}|i}.$$

After canceling the factor $a_{\overline{10}|i}$ the equation becomes

$$55 + 55v^{10} = 30 + 60v^{10} + 90v^{20}.$$

With $v^{10} = y$, this becomes the quadratic equation
$$90y^2 + 5y - 25 = 0,$$
or equivalently $18y^2 + y - 5 = 0$. The roots are $y = .50, -.556$. We ignore the negative root for $v^{10} = y$. Therefore, $v^{10} = .50$ so that $v = (.50)^{.1}$, and then $i = .0718$. Finally, $X = 55a_{\overline{20}|.0718} = 575$.

2.1.18 Option 1 corresponds to a single deposit earning ordinary compound interest (compounded annually), and the accumulated value at the end of 24 years is $10,000(1+i)^{24}$.

Under Option 2, the 10,000 purchases an annuity-immediate at 10% paying K per year, so that $10,000 = Ka_{\overline{24}|.1}$ (the purchase price of 10,000 is the present value of the annuity-immediate being purchased). Solving for K results in

$$K = \frac{10,000}{a_{\overline{24}|.1}} = \frac{10,000(.1)}{1-v_{.1}^{24}} = \frac{1000}{.898474} = 1,113.$$

Under Option 2, the payments of 1,113 will be received at the end of each year for 24 years (it is implicitly understood that with an annuity-immediate the payments begin one period after the annuity is purchased – this is referred to as the "end" of the year). If, as the payments are received, they are deposited into an account earning interest at effective annual interest rate 5%, then the accumulated value of the account at the end of 24 years is

$$1113s_{\overline{24}|.05} = (1.113)\left[\frac{(1.05)^{24}-1}{.05}\right] = (1113)(44.502) = 49,531.$$

Since Option 1 results in the same accumulated value, we have $10,000(1+i)^{24} = 49,531$, from which it follows that $i = .0689$.

2.1.19 The phrase "at the end of each year" indicates an annuity immediate.

$$Xa_{\overline{n}|} = X\left(\tfrac{1-v^n}{i}\right) = 493, \quad 3Xa_{\overline{2n}|} = 3X\left(\tfrac{1-v^{2n}}{i}\right) = 2748.$$

Using the factorization $1-v^{2n} = (1-v^n)(1+v^n)$, we have

$$\frac{3Xa_{\overline{2n}|}}{Xa_{\overline{n}|}} = \frac{3(1-v^{2n})/i}{(1-v^n)/i} = 3(1+v^n) = \frac{2748}{493} = 5.574 \rightarrow v^n = .858.$$

This idea has arisen in exam questions a number of times over the years. A similar factorization could be applied if $s_{\overline{n}|}$ and $s_{\overline{2n}|}$ were given. A more involved situation arises if $a_{\overline{n}|}$ and $a_{\overline{3n}|}$ are given. In that case, we use the factorization

$$1-v^{3n} = (1-v^n)(1+v^n+v^{2n}).$$

2.1.20 $\quad 10{,}000 = K \cdot a_{\overline{10}|.03} + 200v^5 \cdot a_{\overline{5}|.03} \;\rightarrow\; K = 1079.68$

2.1.21 $\quad a_{\overline{n}|} = \dfrac{1-v^n}{i} = \dfrac{1}{i} - v^n \cdot \dfrac{1}{i} = a_{\overline{\infty}|} - v^n \cdot a_{\overline{\infty}|}$

2.1.22 (b) $\quad v^k a_{\overline{n}|i} = v^k[v + v^2 + \cdots + v^n]$

$$= v^{k+1} + v^{k+2} + \cdots + v^{k+n}$$

$$= [v + v^2 + \cdots + v^k + v^{k+1} + v^{k+2} + \cdots + v^{k+n}]$$

$$- [v + v^2 + \cdots + v^k]$$

$$= a_{\overline{n+k}|} - a_{\overline{k}|}$$

2.1.23 $\quad 330.80$

$$PV = 10v^{40}\left[s_{\overline{10}|.05} + s_{\overline{20}|.05} + s_{\overline{30}|.05} + s_{\overline{40}|.05} \right]$$

$$= 10\left[v^{30}a_{\overline{10}|.05} + v^{20}a_{\overline{20}|.05} + v^{10}a_{\overline{30}|.05} + a_{\overline{40}|.05} \right]$$

$$= 10\left[a_{\overline{40}|} - a_{\overline{10}|} + a_{\overline{40}|} - a_{\overline{20}|} + a_{\overline{40}|} - a_{\overline{30}|} + a_{\overline{40}|} \right]$$

2.1.24 $\quad Y = s_{\overline{k}|j} + (1+j)^k s_{\overline{n}|i}, \quad X = a_{\overline{n}|i} + v_i^n \cdot a_{\overline{k}|}$

$$\rightarrow X(1+i)^n \cdot (1+j)^k$$

$$= a_{\overline{n}|i} \cdot (1+i)^n \cdot (1+j)^k + v_i^n \cdot a_{\overline{k}|j} \cdot (1+i)^n \cdot (1+j)^k$$

$$= (1+j)^k s_{\overline{n}|i} + s_{\overline{k}|j}$$

2.1.25 $\dfrac{1}{a_{\overline{n}|i}} = \dfrac{i}{1-v^n} = \dfrac{i-iv^n+iv^n}{1-v^n} = \dfrac{i(1-v^n)}{1-v^n} + \dfrac{iv^n}{1-v^n}$

$$= i + \dfrac{i}{(1+i)^n-1} = i + \dfrac{1}{s_{\overline{n}|i}}$$

2.1.26 $a_{\overline{n}|i} = v^n a_{\overline{2n}|i} \rightarrow \dfrac{v^n a_{\overline{2n}|i}}{a_{\overline{n}|i}} = \dfrac{v^n(1-v^{2n})}{1-v^n}$

$$= v^n(1+v^n) = v^n + v^{2n} = 1$$

$\rightarrow v^{2n} + v^n - 1 = 0 \rightarrow v^n = \dfrac{-1 \pm \sqrt{1+4}}{2} = .6180$ or $-1.6180.$

(discard negative root)

2.1.27 (a) $\ddot{a}_{\overline{n}|i} = \dfrac{1-v^n}{d} = \dfrac{1-v^n}{i/(1+i)} = (1+i) \cdot \dfrac{1-v^n}{i} = (1+i) \cdot a_{\overline{n}|i}$

$$= a_{\overline{n}|i} + i \cdot a_{\overline{n}|i} = a_{\overline{n}|i} + i \cdot \dfrac{1-v^n}{i} = a_{\overline{n}|i} + 1 - v^n$$

$$= 1 + (v + v^2 + \cdots + v^{n-1} + v^n) - v^n$$

$$= 1 + (v + v^2 + \cdots + v^{n-1}) = 1 + a_{\overline{n-1}|i}$$

(b) $\ddot{s}_{\overline{n}|i} = \dfrac{(1+i)^n-1}{d} = \dfrac{(1+i)^n-1}{i/(1+i)} = (1+i) \cdot \dfrac{(1+i)^n-1}{i} = (1+i) \cdot s_{\overline{n}|i}$

$$= s_{\overline{n}|i} + i \cdot s_{\overline{n}|i} = s_{\overline{n}|i} + i \cdot \dfrac{(1+i)^n-1}{i} = s_{\overline{n}|i} + (1+i)^n - 1$$

$$= \left[1 + (1+i) + (1+i)^2 + \cdots + (1+i)^{n-1} + (1+i)^n \right] - 1$$

$$= s_{\overline{n+1}|i} - 1$$

2.1.28 At rate j per month, $5000 = 117.38 a_{\overline{12n}|j} \rightarrow a_{\overline{12n}|j} = 42.5967,$

$10,000 = 113.40 \ddot{s}_{\overline{12n}|j} \rightarrow \ddot{s}_{\overline{12n}|j} = 88.1834.$

Using the identities $\ddot{s}_{\overline{12n}|j} = s_{\overline{12n}|j} - 1 + (1+j)^{12n}$ and

$s_{\overline{12n}|j} = (1+j)^{12n} \cdot a_{\overline{12n}|j}$, we have $(1+j)^{12n} = 2.045646.$

Then $v^{12n} = .488843$, so that $j = \dfrac{1-v^{12n}}{a_{\overline{12n}|j}} = .012.$

Then $i = (1+j)^{12} - 1 = .1539.$

2.1.29 (a) $v_j + v_j \cdot v_i + v_j^2 \cdot v_i + v_j^2 \cdot v_i^2 + v_j^3 \cdot v_i^2 + v_j^3 \cdot v_i^3 + \cdots$

$$= v_j[1+v_i][1+v_j \cdot v_i + (v_j \cdot v_i)^2 + \cdots]$$

$$= v_j[1+v_i] \cdot \frac{1}{1-v_j \cdot v_i}$$

(b) (i) $[v + v^3 + v^5 + \cdots] + 2[v^2 + v^4 + v^6 + \cdots]$

$$= [v + 2v^2][1 + v^2 + v^4 + \cdots] = \frac{v + 2v^2}{1-v^2}$$

(ii) $\dfrac{1+2v}{1-v^2}$

2.1.30 (a) $X = \dfrac{L}{2a_{\overline{10}|} - a_{\overline{5}|}}, \quad Y = \dfrac{L}{a_{\overline{10}|}}, \quad Z = \dfrac{L}{a_{\overline{10}|} + a_{\overline{5}|}}$

$\rightarrow \dfrac{1}{X} = \dfrac{2a_{\overline{10}|} - a_{\overline{5}|}}{L}, \quad \dfrac{3}{2Y} = \dfrac{\frac{3}{2}a_{\overline{10}|}}{L}, \quad \dfrac{1}{Z} = \dfrac{a_{\overline{10}|} + a_{\overline{5}|}}{L}.$

Since $a_{\overline{10}|} < 2a_{\overline{5}|}$ it follows that

$2a_{\overline{10}|} - a_{\overline{5}|} < \frac{3}{2}a_{\overline{10}|} < a_{\overline{10}|} + a_{\overline{5}|}$, so that $\dfrac{1}{X} < \dfrac{3}{2Y} < \dfrac{1}{Z}.$

(b) $P_1 = \dfrac{Li}{1-v_i^n}$ and $P_2 = \dfrac{L \cdot 2i}{1-v_{2i}^n}$. Since $v_i^n > v_{2i}^n$ it follows that

$\dfrac{P_2}{2P_1} = \dfrac{1-v_i^n}{1-v_{2i}^n} < 1.$

2.1.31 $10(X+Y) = 10{,}233 \rightarrow X + Y = 1023.3$

$5000 = Y(v + v^3 + v^5 + \cdots + v^{19}) + X(v^2 + v^4 + v^6 + \cdots + v^{20})$

$\rightarrow 5000 = [vY + v^2 X][1 + v^2 + v^4 + \cdots + v^{18}]$

$$= [vY + v^2 X]\left[\frac{1-v^{20}}{1-v^2}\right] = 4.720263X + 5.097884Y$$

Solving the two equations for X and Y results in $X = 573.76$ and $Y = 449.54$.

2.1.32 $11{,}000 = 367.21 \, [a_{\overline{37}|.01} - v^k] = 11{,}309.89 - 367.21v^k$

$\rightarrow v_{.01}^k = .8439 \rightarrow k = \dfrac{\ln(.8439)}{\ln(v_{.01})} = 17$

2.1.33 (a) $v^t \cdot s_{\overline{n}|} = \dfrac{(1+i)^n - 1}{i} = \dfrac{(1+i)^{n-t} - v^t}{i}$

$$= \dfrac{(1+i)^{n-t} - 1 + 1 - v^t}{i} = a_{\overline{t}|} + s_{\overline{n-t}|}$$

for $t > n$, $v^t \cdot s_{\overline{n}|} = v^{t-n} \cdot v^n \cdot s_{\overline{n}|} = v^{t-n} \cdot a_{\overline{n}|}$

SECTION 2.2

2.2.1 (a) $X = \dfrac{50,000}{a_{\overline{300}|j}} = 447.24$, where $j = (1.05)^{1/6} - 1$ is the one-month effective rate of interest.

(b) $(X + 100)a_{\overline{n}|j} = 50,000 \rightarrow a_{\overline{n}|j} = 91.366987$

$$\rightarrow n = \dfrac{\ln[1 - 91.366987 j]}{\ln[v_j]} = 168.5$$

(or using a calculator function). Then the 168th payment of $X + 100 = 547.24$ occurs on December 31, 2023, and the amount of the additional final payment will be Y where

$547.24 a_{\overline{168}|j} + Y \cdot v_j^{169} = 50,000 \rightarrow Y = 290.30.$

2.2.2 Derek's accumulated value should be

$$1200 \ddot{s}_{\overline{25}|.06} = 1200(1.06) \cdot \dfrac{(1.06)^{25} - 1}{.06} = 69,787.66.$$

Anne's accumulated value should be

$$1200 s_{\overline{25}|.06} = 1200 \cdot \dfrac{(1.06)^{25} - 1}{.06} = 65,837.41.$$

Ira's accumulated value should be $100 \ddot{s}_{\overline{300}|j}$, where

$j = (1.06)^{1/12} - 1 = .00486755$ is the equivalent one-month compound interest rate. Then

$$100 \ddot{s}_{\overline{300}|j} = 100(1.00486755) \cdot \dfrac{(1.00486755)^{300} - 1}{.00486755} = 67,958.10.$$

2.2.3 Quarterly interest rate is j, where $(1.07)^{1/4} - 1 = .01706.$

$450 s_{\overline{40}|j} (1.07)^5 = Y \ddot{a}_{\overline{4}|} \rightarrow Y = 9872.$

2.2.4   We denote the 4-year rate of interest by j. Then the accumulated value at the end of 40 years is $X = 100\ddot{s}_{\overline{10}|j}$ (10 4-year periods, with valuation one full 4-year period after the 10th deposit). The accumulated value at the end of 20 years is $100\ddot{s}_{\overline{5}|j}$. We are given that $100\ddot{s}_{\overline{10}|j} = 5 \times 100\ddot{s}_{\overline{5}|j}$.

This is equivalent to $\dfrac{(1+j)^{10}-1}{d_j} = 5 \times \dfrac{(1+j)^5-1}{d_j}$, where $d_j = \dfrac{j}{1+j}$ is the 4-year discount rate equivalent to the 4-year interest rate j. Factoring the left hand side of the equation, we get

$$\frac{\left[(1+j)^5-1\right]\cdot\left[(1+j)^5+1\right]}{d_j} = 5 \times \frac{(1+j)^5-1}{d_j},$$

from which it follows that $(1+j)^5 + 1 = 5$, and then $(1+j)^5 = 4$ and $j = .3195$, and $d_j = \frac{.3195}{1.3195} = .2421$. Then

$$X = 100\ddot{s}_{\overline{10}|j} = 100 \cdot \frac{(1+j)^{10}-1}{d_j} = 100 \cdot \frac{16-1}{.2421} = 6195.$$

2.2.5   Let $j = 6$-month interest rate, and $d_j = 6$-month discount rate. Then $\ddot{a}_{\overline{\infty}|j} = \frac{1}{d_j} = \frac{1+j}{j} = 20 \rightarrow j = \frac{1}{19}$.

Let $k = 2$-year rate of interest, and $d_k = 2$-year discount rate.

$$X\ddot{a}_{\overline{\infty}|k} = 20 \rightarrow X = 20d_k = 20 \cdot \frac{k}{1+k} = 20\left[\frac{(1+j)^4-1}{(1+j)^4}\right]$$

(since $(1+j)^4 = 1+k$). Therefore $X = 20\left[\frac{\left(1+\frac{1}{19}\right)^4-1}{\left(1+\frac{1}{19}\right)^4}\right] = 3.71$.

2.2.6   Let P be the monthly payment Sally receives from Tim. Since Sally's yield over the 5 years is 3.725% every 6 months, the value of her accumulated deposits at the end of 5 years must be $10,000(1.03725)^{10} = P s_{\overline{60}|.005}$ (the deposits accumulate at ½% per month). Solving for P results in $P = 206.62$. Let k be the monthly rate on Tim's loan. Then $10,000 = 206.62 \cdot a_{\overline{60}|k}$. Using the calculator unknown interest function we get $k = .0073$, so that the nominal annual interest rate on Tim's loan is $12k = .088$.

2.2.7 $10,000(1.05)^n \geq \frac{2000}{.05} = 40,000 \rightarrow (1.05)^n \geq 4$

$$\rightarrow n \geq \frac{\ln(4)}{\ln(1.05)} = 28.4.$$

At time 28 the accumulated value is $10,000(1.05)^{28} = 39,201.29$ and at time 29 the accumulated value is $10,000(1.05)^{29} = 41,161.36$. Since 40,000 is the target value of the fund, a reduced scholarship of 1161.36 can be awarded at time 29 (September 1, 1999), while still allowing for the full payment of 2000 in perpetuity from time 30 (September 1, 2000) on.

2.2.8 Monthly effective interest is at rate $j = .0075$, and effective annual interest is at rate $i = (1.0075)^{12} - 1 = .09380690$. After n complete years the accumulated value is $100\ddot{s}_{\overline{12n}|j} + 1000s_{\overline{n}|i}$. In order for this to exceed 100,000, we must have (using $d_j = \frac{j}{1+j} = .007444$),

$$\ddot{s}_{\overline{12n}|j} + 10s_{\overline{n}|i} = \frac{(1+i)^n - 1}{d_j} + 10 \cdot \frac{(1+i)^n - 1}{i}$$

$$= 240.9353(1+i)^n - 240.9353 \geq 1000.$$

Thus, $(1+i)^n \geq 5.15 \rightarrow n \geq \frac{\ln(5.15)}{\ln(1+i)} = 18.3$.

$n = 18 \rightarrow \ddot{s}_{\overline{216}|j} + 10s_{\overline{18}|i} = 969.2$, and

$n = 19 \rightarrow \ddot{s}_{\overline{228}|j} + 10s_{\overline{19}|i} = 1078.2$.

The account exceeds 100,000 sometime between January 1 and December 31, 2013. The balance on April 1 after the deposit is 99,521, and the balance on April 30 just after interest is 100,268.

2.2.9 $100s_{\overline{n}|.04} = 200a_{\overline{2n}|.04} \rightarrow v^{2n} + v^n - .50 = 0 \rightarrow v^n = .366025$
(ignore negative root) $\rightarrow n = 25.6 \rightarrow 26$ deposits.

2.2.10 $500s_{\overline{n}|.05} \geq 1000s_{\overline{10}|.05}(1.05)^{n-10} \to a_{\overline{n}|.05} \geq 2a_{\overline{10}|.05} \to n \geq 30.32$

On January 1, 2015, Account A has a balance of 33,373 and Account B has a balance of 33,219. On January 1, 2016 the balances are 35,042 and 35,380.

2.2.11 $1000 = 100 \cdot \left[a_{\overline{4}|.035} + v_{.035}^4 \cdot a_{\overline{8}|i} \right] \to a_{\overline{8}|i} = 7.260287.$

Using the unknown interest calculator function we get $i = 2.208\%$.

2.2.12 For the insurer, after expenses, the profit is

$3368.72 \left[(.80)(1.125)^{25} + (.90) \cdot \ddot{s}_{\overline{24}|.125} \right] - 250,000 = 234,829.$

The rate of return earned by the policyholder is i where

$3368.72\ddot{s}_{\overline{25}|i} = 250,000 \to i = .076.$

2.2.13 $12,000 = 592.15a_{\overline{24}|j} = 426.64a_{\overline{36}|j}$

$\to \frac{592.15}{426.64}[1 + v^{12}] = 1 + v^{12} + v^{24} \to v^{12} = .846321$

$\to j = .0140 \to i^{(12)} = .1680.$

$12,000 = K \cdot a_{\overline{48}|j} \to K = 345.02.$

2.2.14 Three-year rate of interest is $j = (1+i)^3 - 1$. PV of perpetuity starting in 6 years (two 3-year periods) is $v_j \cdot \frac{10}{j} = \frac{10}{(1+j)j} = 32$

$\to 32j^2 + 32j - 10 = 0 \to j = .25$ or -1.25 (we ignore negative root). Therefore $(1+i)^3 = 1.25$. Let the 4-month interest rate be k. Then $(1+k)^3 = 1+i = (1.25)^{1/3}$. PV of perpetuity-immediate of 1 every 4 months is $X = \frac{1}{k} = \frac{1}{(1.25)^{1/9} - 1} = 39.84.$

2.2.15 The 2-month effective rate of interest is j.

(a) $25a_{\overline{36}|j} = 150a_{\overline{6}|.06}^{(6)} = 755.83$, where $j = (1.06)^{1/6} - 1$

(b) $25v_j^4 a_{\overline{36}|j} = 50v_{.02}^2 a_{\overline{18}|.02}^{(2)} = 724.08$, where $j = (1.02)^{1/2} - 1$

(c) $25(1+j)s_{\overline{36}|j} = 1092.02$, where $j = (.97)^{-1/3} - 1$

(d) $25(1+j)^6 s_{\overline{36}|j} = 1144.57$, where $j = e^{.01} - 1$

2.2.16 The series is the same as a perpetuity-immediate of 1 per month plus a perpetuity-immediate of 1 per year. At monthly rate j the present value of the monthly perpetuity is $\frac{1}{j}$, and the present value of the annual perpetuity is $\frac{1}{i}$, where $i = (1+j)^{12} - 1 = j \cdot s_{\overline{12}|j}$ is the equivalent effective annual rate of interest.

2.2.17 $\int_0^u \delta_y \, dy = \int_0^u \left[p + \frac{se^{-st}}{e^{-st} + r} \right] dt = pu - \ln\left[\frac{e^{-su} + r}{1+r} \right]$

$\rightarrow e^{-\int_0^u \delta_y \, dy} = \left[\frac{e^{-su} + r}{1+r} \right] \cdot e^{-pu}$

$\rightarrow \overline{a}_{\overline{n}|} = \int_0^n \left[\frac{e^{-su} + r}{1+r} \right] \cdot e^{-pu} \, du = \frac{r(1-e^{-pn})}{(1+r)p} + \frac{(1-e^{-(p+s)n})}{(1+r)(p+s)}$

2.2.18 $L = K' \cdot a_{\overline{n/2}|i} \rightarrow$

$K' = \frac{L}{a_{\overline{n/2}|i}} = \frac{Lj}{1 - v^{n/2}} = \frac{Lj}{1-v^n}[1 + v^{n/2}]$

$= \frac{L}{a_{\overline{n}|i}}[1 + v^{n/2}]$

$= K[1 + v^{n/2}] \leq 2K$

2.2.19 (a)   The 6-month effective interest rate is

$$j = (1.01)^3 - 1 = .030301.$$

$$500 s_{\overline{n}|j} = 10,000 \rightarrow n = \frac{\left[\ln\left[1 + \frac{10,000 j}{500}\right]\right]}{\ln(1+j)} = 15.87.$$

With the 15th deposit (January 1, 2006, the balance is $500 s_{\overline{15}|j} = 9320.00$. With interest (1% every 2 months)

on February 28 the balance is $9320.00(1.01) = 9413.20$, on April 30 it is 9507.33, and on June 30 it is 9602.41. On July 1, 2006, the deposit of 500 brings the balance to 10,102.41.

(b) The 6-month effective interest rate is
$$j = (1.04)^{1/2} - 1 = .01980390.$$

$n = 17.01$. With the 17th deposit the balance is 9989.75.
$9989.75[1 + (.04)t] = 10,000 \rightarrow t = .025652$ years, or 9.4 days. Close the account on January 11, 2007.

2.2.20 (a) $s_{\overline{20}|.03}(1.04)^n + s_{\overline{n}|.04} \geq 100 \rightarrow 51.870375(1.04)^n \geq 125$
$\rightarrow n \geq 22.4$ (23)

(b) $s_{\overline{n}|.03}(1.04)^n + s_{\overline{n}|.04} \geq 100.$
Trial and error:
$n = 21 \rightarrow 97.316;$ $n = 22 \rightarrow 106.618.$

2.2.21 $n \cdot \ln(1.0075) = .008333 n - \frac{(.008333)^2 \cdot n^2}{2} \rightarrow n = 24.8$

$n \cdot \ln(1.0075) = .008333 n - \frac{(.008333)^2 \cdot n^2}{2} + \frac{(.008333)^3 \cdot n^3}{3}$

$\rightarrow n = 29.7$ or 300.6 (300.6 is an unrealistic answer)

2.2.22 $\quad B = A + (1+i)^n \;\rightarrow\; (1+i)^n = B - A$

$\qquad \rightarrow A = \dfrac{(1+i)^n - 1}{i} = \dfrac{B - A - 1}{i} \;\rightarrow\; i = \dfrac{B - A - 1}{A}$

2.2.23 (a) Follows from the Intermediate Value Theorem of calculus.

(b) (i) $\lim\limits_{i \to \infty} s_{\overline{n}|i} = \infty$, (ii) $\lim\limits_{i \to -1} s_{\overline{n}|i} = 0$, and (iii) $s_{\overline{n}|i}$ is an increasing function of i. If $J, n > 0$ and $M > 0$, then the equation has a unique solution for i.

2.2.24 $\quad (1+i)A + (B - A - I)\overline{s}_{\overline{1}|i} = B \;\rightarrow\; (1+i)A + (B - A - I)\left(1 + \tfrac{i}{2}\right) \doteq B$

$\qquad \rightarrow i \doteq \dfrac{2I}{A + B - I}$

2.2.25 (a) $s_{\overline{n}|i} = \dfrac{(1+i)^n - 1}{i} = \dfrac{\left[(1+j)^m\right]^n - 1}{(1+j)^m - 1}$

$\qquad \ddot{s}_{\overline{n}|i} = \dfrac{(1+i)^n - 1}{1 - v_i} = \dfrac{\left[(1+j)^m\right]^n - 1}{1 - v_j^m}$

$\qquad \ddot{a}_{\overline{n}|i} = \ddot{s}_{\overline{n}|i} \cdot v_j^{m \cdot n} = \dfrac{1 - v_j^{m \cdot n}}{1 - v_j^m}$

(b) $s_{\overline{n}|i} = \dfrac{\left[(1+j)^m\right]^n - 1}{(1+j)^m - 1} = \dfrac{\dfrac{\left[(1+j)^m\right]^n - 1}{i}}{\dfrac{(1+j)^m - 1}{i}} = \dfrac{s_{\overline{mn}|j}}{s_{\overline{m}|j}}$

(c) $1 + i = e^{\delta} \;\rightarrow\; s_{\overline{n}|i} = \dfrac{(1+i)^n - 1}{i} = \dfrac{e^{n\delta} - 1}{e^{\delta} - 1}$

(d) $a_{\overline{\infty}|i} = \dfrac{1}{i} = \dfrac{1}{(1+j)^m - 1} = \dfrac{a_{\overline{\infty}|j}}{s_{\overline{m}|j}}$

$\qquad \ddot{a}_{\overline{\infty}|i} = \dfrac{1}{d} = \dfrac{1}{1 - v_j^m} = \dfrac{a_{\overline{\infty}|j}}{a_{\overline{m}|j}}$

2.2.26 $1+i = (1+j)^m$ $\qquad$ $1+j = (1+i)^{1/m}$ $\qquad$ $v_i = v_j^m$ $\qquad$ $v_j = v_i^{1/m}$

(a) $\dfrac{1}{m} \cdot s_{\overline{nm}|j} = \dfrac{1}{m} \cdot \dfrac{(1+j)^{nm} - 1}{j} = \dfrac{1}{m} \cdot \dfrac{(1+i)^n - 1}{(1+i)^{1/m} - 1}$

2.2.27 (a) $\displaystyle\lim_{m\to\infty} s_{\overline{n}|i}^{(m)} = \lim_{m\to\infty} \dfrac{(1+i)^n - 1}{i^{(m)}} = \dfrac{(1+i)^n - 1}{\displaystyle\lim_{m\to\infty} i^{(m)}} = \dfrac{(1+i)^n - 1}{i^{(\infty)}}$

(b) Since $d < d^{(m)} < \delta < i^{(m)} < i$, it follows that

$$a_{\overline{n}|i} < a_{\overline{n}|i}^{(m)} < \overline{a}_{\overline{n}|i} < \ddot{a}_{\overline{n}|i}^{(m)} < \ddot{a}_{\overline{n}|i}.$$

(c) $\overline{s}_{\overline{n}|i} = \displaystyle\int_0^1 \left[1 + i(1-t)\right] dt = 1 + \dfrac{i}{2}$

SECTION 2.3

2.3.1 The annuity is paid monthly, and the interest rate is quoted as .5% per month, but the geometric increase in the payments occurs once per year. In order to use the geometric payment annuity present

value formula $K\left[\dfrac{1 - \left(\frac{1+r}{1+j}\right)^n}{j - r}\right]$, the payment period, interest period

and geometric growth period must coincide. In a situation such as this, where those periods do not coincide, it is necessary to conform to the geometric growth period, which, in this case, is one year with $r = .05$. The equivalent interest rate per year is the effective annual rate $i = (1.005)^{12} - 1 = .06168$. Since the payments are at the ends of successive months, for each year we must find a single payment at the end of each year that is equivalent to the monthly payments for that year. For the first year, the single payment at the end of the year that is equivalent in value to the 12 monthly payments during the first year is $2000s_{\overline{12}|.005} = 24{,}671 = K$.

The monthly payments in the second year are each $2000(1.05)$, so that the single payment at the end of the second year that is equivalent in value to the 12 monthly payments during the second year is $2000(1.05)s_{\overline{12}|.005} = 24{,}677(1.05) = K(1.05)$. In a similar way, the single payments at the ends of the successive years that are equivalent in value to the monthly payments during those year are K, $K(1.05)$, $K(1.05)^2,\ldots, K(1.05)^{19}$ (the 20th year would have had 19 years of growth in the payment amount). Now, we have interest period, (equivalent) payment period and geometric growth period all being 1 year, so that the present value of the annuity, valued one year before the first equivalent annual payment, is

$$K\left[\frac{1-\left(\frac{(1+r)}{1+i}\right)^n}{i-r}\right] \;=\; (24{,}671)\left[\frac{1-\left(\frac{1.05}{1.06168}\right)^{20}}{.06168-.05}\right] = 419{,}242.$$

This answer is based on some roundoff. If exact calculator values are used, the answer is 419,253.

2.3.2   (i) $1000\left[(1.01)^{29} +(.99)(1.01)^{28} +\cdots+(.99)^{29}\right]$

$$= 1000(1.01)^{29}\left[\frac{1-\left(\frac{.99}{1.01}\right)^{30}}{1-\frac{.99}{1.01}}\right] = 30{,}407$$

(ii) 59,704

(iii) 151,906

2.3.3 $k\% = .01k$ in decimal form. The present value of the perpetuity-immediate is $30a_{\overline{\infty}|.01k} = \dfrac{30}{.01k}$. The 10-year annuity has geometrically increasing payments, with $r=.01k$, and the valuation rate for present value is $i=.01k$. Since $i=r$, the present value of the geometrically increasing annuity is

$$Knv = (53)(10)\left(\frac{1}{1+.01k}\right) = \frac{530}{1+.01k}.$$

We are told that Jeff and Jason each use the same amount to purchase their annuities, and therefore $\dfrac{30}{.01k} = \dfrac{530}{1+.01k}$. Solving for k results in $k = 6(\%)$.

2.3.4 PV $=$ $10v + 10v^2 + 10v^3 + 10v^4 + 10v^5$

$$+ 10(1+.01K)v^6 + 10(1+.01K)^2 v^7 + \cdots$$

$$= 10a_{\overline{4}|.092} + 10v^4 \left[v + (1+.01K)v^2 + (1+.01K)^2 v^3 + \cdots \right]$$

$$= 10a_{\overline{4}|.092} + 10v^4 \frac{1}{i - .01K} \;=\; 167.50 \;\rightarrow\; K = 4.$$

2.3.5   In order to use the geometric payment annuity formula, the payment period, interest period and geometric growth period must all coincide. In this case the payments are monthly and the geometric growth (inflation) is annual. We deal with this situation by determining a single annual payment at the end of each year which is equal to the accumulated value of the 12 monthly payments for that year. Suppose that first year's monthly payment is R. Then a single payment at the end of the year that is equivalent to the 12 month-end payments is $Rs_{\overline{12}|j}$, where j is the monthly interest rate that is found from the equation $(1+j)^{12} = 1.06$. Therefore, the equivalent annual payment for the first year is $Rs_{\overline{12}|j} = 12.3265R$.

In the second year the monthly payments are $1.032R$, so the single payment at the end of the second year that is equivalent to the monthly payments in the second year is

$$1.032Rs_{\overline{12}|j} = (1.032)(12.3265R).$$

In the same way we can see that the monthly payment in the third year is equivalent to a single year end payment of

$$(1.032)^2 Rs_{\overline{12}|j} = (1.032)^2 (12.3265R).$$

This pattern continues to the 20th year, when the monthly payment is equivalent to a single year end payment of

$$(1.032)^{19} Rs_{\overline{12}|j} = (1.032)^{19} (12.3265R).$$

The present value of the equivalent annual payments is

$$12.3265R \cdot \left[\frac{1-\left(\frac{1.032}{1.06}\right)^{20}}{.06-.032} \right].$$

We are told that the buyout package (present value) has a value of 100,000.

Therefore $12.3265R \cdot \left[\dfrac{1-\left(\frac{1.032}{1.06}\right)^{20}}{.06-.032} \right] = 100,000$, from which we get $R = 548$.

2.3.6 (a) $(1+r)^n \ddot{s}_{\overline{n}|j} = (1+r)^n \dfrac{\left(\frac{1+i}{1+r}\right)^n - 1}{1+\frac{1+r}{1+i}} = \dfrac{(1+i)^n - (1+r)^n}{1-\frac{1+r}{1+i}}$

$AV = (1+i)^n \cdot PV = \dfrac{(1+i)^n - (1+r)^n}{1-\frac{1+r}{1+i}}$

(b) Use $\dfrac{1}{1+i} = \dfrac{1}{1+r} v_j$

2.3.7 $100,000 = 2000(v+v^2+v^3)\left[1+v^3(1+r)+v^6(1+r)+\cdots\right]$

$= \dfrac{2000a_{\overline{3}|.045}}{1-v^3(1+r)} \rightarrow r = .0784$

2.3.8 (a) Final salary is $18,000(1.04)^{36} = 73,871$. Total career salary is $18,000\left[1+(1.04)+(1.04)^2+\cdots+(1.04)^{36}\right] = 18,000s_{\overline{37}|.04}$ $= 1,470,640$, so career average annual salary is 39,747. Pension is $(.70)(39,747) = 27,823 = (.377)(73,871)$.

(b) $(37)(.025)(39,747) = 36,766$

(c) Average salary in final 10 years is
$$(.10)(18,000)\left[(1.04)^{27} + (1.04)^{28} + \cdots + (1.04)^{36}\right] = 62,312$$
Pension is $(.025)(37)(62,312) = 57,639$.

(d) Accumulated amount after 37 years is
$$(.06)(18,000)\left[(1.06)^{36} + (1.04)(1.06)^{35}\right.$$
$$\left. + \cdots + (1.04)^{36}\right](1.06)^{1/2}$$
$$= (.06)(18,000)(1.06)^{36}\left[\frac{1 - \left(\frac{1.04}{1.06}\right)^{37}}{1 - \frac{1.04}{1.06}}\right](1.06)^{1/2} = 242,845.$$
Then $242,845 = X \cdot \ddot{a}_{\overline{20}|.06} \;\rightarrow\; X = 19,974$.

2.3.9　The total payout over 20 years is
$$2000 \times 12 \times \left[1 + 1.03 + (1.03)^2 + \cdots + (1.03)^{19}\right]$$
$$= 24,000 \times \frac{(1.03)^{20} - 1}{1.03 - 1} = 644,889.$$

Note that in the 20th year, there will have been 19 annual inflationary increases since the first year. We formulate the present value in a way that is similar to that in Example 2.18 and in Exercise 2.3.5 above. The value at the end of each year of that year's payments is $P \cdot s_{\overline{12}|j}$, where $j = (1+i)^{1/12} - 1$ is the equivalent monthly rate of interest and P is the monthly payment. The monthly payments are 2000 in the first year, $2000(1.03)$ in the second year, $2000(1.03)^2$ in the third year,..., $2000(1.03)^{19}$ in the 20th year. Now using the equivalent annual payment at the end of each year, the present value is

$$2000 \cdot s_{\overline{12}|j} \times \left[v_i + (1.03)v_i^2 + (1.03)^2 v_i^3 + \cdots + (1.03)^{19} v_i^{20}\right]$$
$$= 2000 \cdot s_{\overline{12}|j} \times \frac{1 - \left(\frac{1.03}{1+i}\right)^{20}}{i - .03}.$$

We set this equal to the given present value of 346,851 and solve for i. This requires a numerical solution. MS EXCEL Solver gives a solution of $i = .0640$.

2.3.10 $X = Z\left[7+.05(Is)_{\overline{6}|.06}\right] = 8.1615Z,$

$Y = Z\left[14+.025(Is)_{\overline{13}|.03}\right]$

$\qquad = 16.5719Z \;\rightarrow\; \dfrac{Y}{X}$

$\qquad = \dfrac{16.57}{8.16}$

$\qquad = 2.03.$

2.3.11   Sandy's annuity has present value
$$90a_{\overline{\infty}|i} + 10(Ia)_{\overline{\infty}|i} \;=\; \tfrac{90}{i} + 10\left(\tfrac{1}{i} + \tfrac{1}{i^2}\right).$$
Danny's annuity has present value $180\ddot{a}_{\overline{\infty}|i} \;=\; \dfrac{180}{d}.$

We are told that $\dfrac{90}{i} + 10\left(\tfrac{1}{i} + \tfrac{1}{i^2}\right) \;=\; \dfrac{180(1+i)}{i}.$

We solve the quadratic equation $18i^2 + 8i - 1 = 0$ which results in $i = .102$ (ignore the negative root $-.346$).

2.3.12   With monthly rate j, $X = 2(Ia)_{\overline{60}|j}.$

We are given 3-month rate

$.0225 \;\rightarrow\; (1+j)^3 = 1.0225 \;\rightarrow\; j = .007444.$

$$X \;=\; 2 \cdot \dfrac{\ddot{a}_{\overline{60}|.00744} - 60v^{60}_{.007444}}{.007444} \;=\; 2729.$$

2.3.13 The progression of fund X and deposits to fund Y are described in the following timeline.

Fund X *earns* interest at rate 6%.

	Amount in Fund X	Deposit to Fund Y	Fund Y Interest
0	1000		
1	900	100	+60
2	800	100	+54
3	700	100	+48
4	600	100	+42
5	500	100	+36
6	400	100	+30
7	300	100	+24
8	200	100	+18
9	100	100	+12
10	0	100	+6

The deposits into Fund Y consist of a combination of level deposits of 100 each for 10 years, along with decreasing deposits. The accumulated value in Fund Y is

$$100 s_{\overline{10}|.09} + 6(Ds)_{\overline{10}|.09} = 1519.30 + 565.38 = 2085.$$

2.3.14 The timeline of the payments is

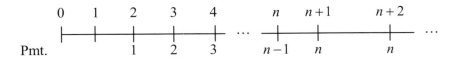

The schedule of payments can be written as the combination of two series

Time	1	2	3	4	$\cdots$	n	$n+1$	$n+2$	
	n	n	n	n	$\cdots$	n	n	n	$\cdots$
	$-n$	$-(n-1)$	$-(n-2)$	$-(n-3)$	$\cdots$	-1			

In other words, the perpetuity can be written as a level perpetuity immediate of n per year <u>minus</u> a decreasing n-year annuity-immediate whose payments start at n and decrease by 1 per year.

The present value of the perpetuity can be formulated as the combination of the two present values.

$$PV = na_{\overline{\infty}|.105} - (Da)_{\overline{n}|.105} = n\left(\frac{1}{.105}\right) - \frac{n-a_{\overline{n}|}}{.105} = \frac{a_{\overline{n}|}}{.105} = 77.1.$$

Therefore $a_{\overline{n}|.105} = 8.0955 \rightarrow n = 19.$

2.3.15 $\quad 12{,}000 = 395a_{\overline{36}|.01} + X\left[a_{\overline{12}|.01} - v^{24}a_{\overline{12}|.01}\right] \rightarrow X = 44.98$

2.3.16 $\quad A + nB, A + (n-1)B, A + (n-2)B, \ldots, A + 2B, A + B$

The series of payments is $100, 97, 94, \ldots, 31, 28 \equiv 25 + (25)(3),$

$25 + (24)(3), 25 + (23)(3), \ldots, 25 + (2)(3), 25 + 3.$ the PV is

$25a_{\overline{25}|} + 3(Da)_{\overline{25}|}.$

2.3.17 $\quad$ If the deposits had been made at the 8% rate then the accumulated value at the end of 20 years would be $300\ddot{s}_{\overline{20}|.08} = 14{,}827.$ The actual investment accumulates to

$$300(20) + 300i(Is)_{\overline{20}|i/2} = 6000 + 300i\left[\frac{\ddot{s}_{\overline{20}|i/2} - 20}{i/2}\right]$$

$$= 6000 + 600\left[\ddot{s}_{\overline{20}|i/2} - 20\right],$$

and we set this equal to 14,827. Therefore

$$6000 + 600\left[\ddot{s}_{\overline{20}|i/2} - 20\right] = 14{,}827 \rightarrow \ddot{s}_{\overline{20}|i/2}$$

$$= 34.71 \rightarrow \frac{i}{2} = .05.$$

2.3.18 PV of Annuity 2 $= 2 \times$ (PV of Annuity 1)

$\to 11a_{\overline{\infty}|} - (Da)_{\overline{10}|} = 2(Da)_{\overline{10}|}$

$\to 3(Da)_{\overline{10}|} = 11a_{\overline{\infty}|} \to 3\left[\dfrac{10 - a_{\overline{10}|}}{i}\right] = \dfrac{11}{i}$

$\to 3a_{\overline{10}|} = 19 \to a_{\overline{10}|} = \dfrac{19}{3} \to i = .093 \to (Da)_{\overline{10}|} = 39.4.$

2.3.19 If j is the monthly effective interest rate, i the effective annual interest rate and r the annual inflation rate used for valuation purposes, then the present value of the perpetuity-immediate is $\dfrac{400s_{\overline{12}|j}}{i - r}$.

(i) PV before deindexing $= 168{,}620$, PV after deindexing $= 84{,}310$

(ii) PV before deindexing $= 56{,}207$, PV after deindexing $= 42{,}155$

(iii) PV before deindexing $= 166{,}497$, PV after deindexing $= 83{,}249$

(iv) PV before deindexing $= 164{,}354$, PV after deindexing $= 82{,}177$

2.3.20 (a) $500{,}000 = 1000 \cdot nv \to n = 505$

(b) Balance just after t^{th} withdrawal is

$1000(1.01)^t \left[v + (1.01)v^2 + \cdots + (1.01)^{504-t} v^{505-t}\right]$

$= 1000(1.01)^t (505-t)v = f(t).$

$f'(t) = 1000v(1.01)^t \left[(505-t) \cdot \ln(1.01) - 1\right] = 0$

$\to t = 505 - \dfrac{1}{\ln(1.01)} = 404.5$

At $t = 404$ the balance is

$1000(1.01)^{404}(505-404)v = 5{,}569{,}741$, and at $t = 405$ the

balance is $1000(1.01)^{405}(505-405)v = 5{,}569{,}741$

2.3.21 (a) $100{,}000 = 6250a_{\overline{20}|} + 750(Ia)_{\overline{20}|}: i = .1014$

(b) $100{,}000 = 7000\left[\dfrac{1-\left(\frac{1.10}{1+i}\right)^{20}}{i-.10}\right]: i = .1266$

2.3.22 (a) $X = (1+i)^{n-1} + 2(1+i)^{n-2} + 3(1+i)^{n-3} + \cdots + (n-1)(1+i) + n$

$(1+i)X = (1+i)^{n} + 2(1+i)^{n-1} + 3(1+i)^{n-2}$

$\qquad\qquad\qquad\qquad + \cdots + (n-1)(1+i)^{2} + n(1+i)$

$\rightarrow\ iX = (1+i)^{n} + (1+i)^{n-1} + (1+i)^{n-2} + \cdots + (1+i) - n = \ddot{s}_{\overline{n}|i} - n$

(b) $s_{\overline{n+1}|i}$ is $n+1$ payments of 1 each plus interest on an increasing total deposit.

2.3.23 (a) $(Ia)_{\overline{n}|} + (Da)_{\overline{n}|}$

$\qquad = (v + 2v^{2} + 3v^{3} + \cdots + (n-1)v^{n-1} + nv^{n})$

$\qquad\quad + \left(nv + (n-1)v^{2} + (n-2)v^{3} + \cdots + 2v^{n-1} + v^{n}\right)$

$\qquad = (n+1)v + (n+1)v^{2} + (n+1)v^{3} + \cdots + (n+1)v^{n}$

$\qquad = (n+1)a_{\overline{n}|}$

(b) $\displaystyle\sum_{k=0}^{n-1} {}_{k|}a_{\overline{n-k}|} = \sum_{k=0}^{n-1} v^{k} \cdot \dfrac{1-v^{n-k}}{i}$

$\qquad\qquad\qquad = \displaystyle\sum_{k=0}^{n-1} \dfrac{v^{k} - v^{n}}{i}$

$\qquad\qquad\qquad = \dfrac{\ddot{a}_{\overline{n}|} - nv^{n}}{i}$

$\qquad\qquad\qquad = (Ia)_{\overline{n}|}$

2.3.24 $(Ia)_{\overline{\infty}|} = \lim_{n \to \infty} (Ia)_{\overline{n}|} = \lim_{n \to \infty} \dfrac{\ddot{a}_{\overline{n}|} - n \cdot v^n}{i}$

$$= \dfrac{\ddot{a}_{\overline{\infty}|}}{i} - \lim_{n \to \infty} \dfrac{n \cdot v^n}{i}$$

$$= \dfrac{1}{d \cdot i} - 0$$

The increasing perpetuity immediate can be looked at as a combination of a level perpetuity immediate of 1 per year, and each year another perpetuity immediate of 1 per year starts up, so that the annual payment grows by 1 every year forever.

2.3.25 (a) (i) $\dfrac{d}{di}(v + v^2 + v^3 + \cdots + v^n)$

$$= \dfrac{d}{di}\left[(1+i)^{-1} + (1+i)^{-2} + (1+i)^{-3} + \cdots + (1+i)^{-n}\right]$$

$$= -(1+i)^{-2} - 2(1+i)^{-3} - 3(1+i)^{-4} - \cdots - n(1+i)^{-n-1}$$

$$= -v(Ia)_{\overline{n}|}$$

(b) $\dfrac{d}{dn} \int_0^n v^t\, dt = v^n$

2.3.26 Using the chain rule with $K = \dfrac{100{,}000}{a_{\overline{300}|\,j}}$

$\rightarrow \dfrac{d}{di^{(2)}} K = \dfrac{100{,}000 v_j (Ia)_{\overline{300}|\,j}}{\left[a_{\overline{300}|\,j}\right]^2} \cdot \dfrac{d}{di^{(2)}} j$, and

$\dfrac{d}{di^{(2)}} j = \dfrac{d}{di^{(2)}}\left[\left(1 + \dfrac{i^{(2)}}{2}\right)^{1/6} - 1\right] = \dfrac{1}{12}\left(1 + \dfrac{i^{(2)}}{2}\right)^{-5/6}$.

The numerical values of the derivative are

$i^{(2)} = .21 \rightarrow \dfrac{d}{di^{(2)}} K = 7459.13$ (or 74.59 per 1% increase in $i^{(2)}$)

$i^{(2)} = .13 \rightarrow \dfrac{d}{di^{(2)}} K = 7101.66$ (or 71.02 per 1% increase in $i^{(2)}$).

2.3.27 Balance December 31, 2004 is $500,000(1+i)$; withdrawal January 1, 2005 is $\frac{500,000(1+i)}{19}$, leaving a balance of $\frac{18}{19} \cdot 500,000(1+i)$. Balance December 31, 2005 is $\frac{18}{19} \cdot 500,000(1+i)^2$; withdrawal January 1, 2006 is $\frac{18}{19} \cdot \frac{500,000(1+i)^2}{18} = \frac{500,000(1+i)^2}{19}$, leaving a balance of $\frac{17}{19} \cdot 500,000(1+i)^2$. Withdrawal on January 1, $2004+t$ is $\frac{500,000(1+i)^t}{19}$.

2.3.28 (a) $100,000 = 1000 a_{\overline{n}|.0075}$

$\to n = 185.5$

$\to 100,000 = 1000 a_{\overline{185}|.0075} + Xv^{186}$

$\to X = 532.46$

(b) $100,000 = 990 a_{\overline{n}|.0075} + 10(Ia)_{\overline{n}|.0075}$

$\to$ (by trial and error) $n = 99$

$\to 100,000 = 990 a_{\overline{99}|.0075} + 10(Ia)_{\overline{99}|.0075} + Xv^{100}$

$\to X = 761.19$

(c) $100,000 = \frac{1000}{1.01} a_{\overline{n}|j}$,

where $v_j = \frac{1.01}{1.0075}$

$\to n = 90$

$\to 100,000 = \frac{1000}{1.01} a_{\overline{90}|j} + Xv^{91}_{.0075}$

$\to X = 93.85$

(d) Total withdrawn: (a)185,532, (b) 148,271, (c)144,957. The more rapidly the payments increase, the more quickly the account is exhausted and the smaller the total withdrawn.

2.3.29 $100(Is)_{\overline{12|}}(1+i)^6 = 17{,}177.70$. At $i = .08$, the left-hand side is $16{,}851.21$ and at $i = .085$ it is $17{,}679.23$. By interpolation we get $i \doteq .08197$ (the exact value is $.0820$).

2.3.30 For each $t < \left(\frac{n+1}{2}\right)$, $tv^t + (n-t+1)v^{n-t+1} < \left(\frac{n+1}{2}\right)v^t + \left(\frac{n+1}{2}\right)v^{n-t+1}$.

This is true since $t < \left(\frac{n+1}{2}\right)$ implies that $n - t + 1 > t$ so that $\left[\frac{n+1}{2} - t\right]v^{n-t+1} < \left[\frac{n+1}{2} - t\right]v^t$, which is equivalent to $tv^t + (n-t+1)v^{n-t+1} < \left(\frac{n+1}{2}\right)v^t + \left(\frac{n+1}{2}\right)v^{n-t+1}$. Then

$$
\begin{aligned}
(Ia)_{\overline{n|}} &= v + 2v^2 + 3v^3 + \cdots + (n-1)v^{n-1} + nv^n \\
&= [v+nv^n] + \left[2v^2 + (n-1)v^{n-1}\right] + \cdots \\
&< \left(\frac{n+1}{2}\right)\left[(v+v^n) + (v^2 + v^{n-1}) + \cdots\right] \\
&= \left(\frac{n+1}{2}\right)a_{\overline{n|}}.
\end{aligned}
$$

2.3.31 (a) $PV = X = 1 + 2v^k + 3v^{2k} + 4v^{3k} + \cdots$

$Xv^k = v^k + 2v^{2k} + 3v^{3k} + \cdots$

$\rightarrow X(1-v^k) = 1 + v^k + v^{2k} + v^{3k} + \cdots = \dfrac{1}{1-v^k}$

$\rightarrow X = \dfrac{1}{(1-v^k)^2} = \dfrac{1}{(ia_{\overline{k|}})^2}$

(b) $Y = (1 + v + v^2 + \cdots + v^{k-1}) + 2(v^k + v^{k+1} + v^{k+2} + \cdots + v^{2k-1})$

$\qquad + 3(v^{2k} + v^{2k+1} + v^{2k+2} + \cdots + v^{3k-1}) + \cdots$

$\qquad = \ddot{a}_{\overline{k|}}\left[1 + 2v^k + 3v^{2k} + \cdots\right] = \dfrac{\ddot{a}_{\overline{k|}}}{(ia_{\overline{k|}})^2}$ (from part (a))

2.3.32 Since all t_r's and K_r's are > 0, $f(i)$ in Example 2.23 is a decreasing function of i, and $f(0) = \sum\limits_{r=1}^{n} K_r$. Thus, in solving $f(i) = L$, if $f(i) = L > \sum\limits_{r=1}^{n} K_r$ then $i < 0$, and if $f(i) = L < \sum\limits_{r=1}^{n} K_r$, then $i > 0$.

2.3.33 Let $f(i) = K_1(1+i)^{t_n-t_1} + K_2(1+i)^{t_n-t_2} + \cdots + K_{n-1}(1+i)^{t_n-t_{n-1}} + K_n$. Since $t_n > t_r$ for $r < n$, it follows that $f(i)$ is an increasing function of i. Also, $\lim\limits_{i \to -1} f(i) = 0$ and $\lim\limits_{i \to \infty} f(i) = \infty$. It follows that if $L > 0$, there is a unique $i > -1$ for which $f(i) = L$.

2.3.34 $\begin{aligned} PV &= 1 + (1+2)v + (1+2+3)v^2 + (1+2+3+4)v^3 + \cdots \\ &= [1 + v + v^2 + v^3 + \cdots] + 2v[1 + v + v^2 + \cdots] \\ &\qquad\qquad + 3v^2[1 + v + v^2 + \cdots] + \cdots \\ &= [1 + v + v^2 + v^3 + \cdots][1 + 2v + 3v^2 + \cdots] = \ddot{a}_{\overline{\infty}|}(I\ddot{a})_{\overline{\infty}|} \end{aligned}$

2.3.35 $\begin{aligned} PV &= v + 2v^2 + 3v^3 + \cdots + (n-1)v^{n-1} + nv^n + (n-1)v^{n+1} \\ &\qquad\qquad + \cdots + 2v^{2n-2} + v^{2n-1} \\ &= [v + v^2 + v^3 + \cdots + v^n] + [v^2 + v^3 + \cdots + v^{n+1}] \\ &\qquad + [v^3 + v^4 + \cdots + v^{n+1}] \\ &\qquad\qquad + \cdots + [v^n + v^{n+1} + v^{n+2} + \cdots + v^{2n-1}] \\ &= a_{\overline{n}|}[1 + v + v^2 + \cdots + v^{n-1}] = a_{\overline{n}|}\ddot{a}_{\overline{n}|} \end{aligned}$

2.3.36 $\begin{aligned} PV &= v + 2v^2 + 2v^3 + \cdots + (n-1)v^{n-1} + nv^n + nv^{n+1} + nv^{n+2} + \cdots \\ &= (Ia)_{\overline{n}|} + nv^n(v + v^2 + v^3 + \cdots) = \frac{\ddot{a}_{\overline{n}|} - nv^n}{i} + nv^n \cdot \frac{1}{i} \end{aligned}$

2.3.37 (a) $\lim_{m\to\infty} (I^{(m)}a)_{\overline{n}|}^{(m)} = \lim_{m\to\infty} \frac{\ddot{a}_{\overline{n}|}^{(m)} - nv^n}{i^{(m)}} = \frac{\overline{a}_{\overline{n}|} - nv^n}{\delta} = (\overline{I}\,\overline{a})_{\overline{n}|}.$

(b) $(\overline{I}\,\overline{a})_{\overline{n}|}$ is the present value of an n-year continuously payable annuity for which the rate of payment is 1 per year during the first year, the rate of payment is 2 per year during the second year, etc.

2.3.38 The accumulated value at time t is

$$F_t = F_0 \cdot e^{\delta t} + \int_0^t h(s) \cdot e^{\delta(t-s)} \, ds.$$

Then,

$$\frac{d}{dt} F_t = F_0 \cdot \delta e^{\delta t} + h(t) \cdot e^{\delta(t-t)} + \int_0^t h(s) \cdot e^{\delta(t-s)} \cdot \delta \, ds = \delta F_t + h(t).$$

2.3.39 (a) $(\overline{D}\overline{a})_{\overline{n}|} = \int_0^n (n-t)v^t \, dt$

$= \int_0^n (n-t) \, d\left(\frac{v^t}{\ln v}\right)$

$= (n-t)\left(\frac{v^t}{\ln v}\right)\Big|_0^n - \int_0^n \left(-\frac{v^t}{\ln v}\right) dt$

$= -\frac{n}{\ln v} + \frac{\overline{a}_{\overline{n}|}}{\ln v}$

$= \frac{\overline{a}_{\overline{n}|} - n}{-\delta}$

$= \frac{n - \overline{a}_{\overline{n}|}}{\delta}$

$(\overline{I}\overline{a})_{\overline{n}|} + (\overline{D}\overline{a})_{\overline{n}|} = \int_0^n tv^t \, dt + \int_0^n (n-t)v^t \, dt$

$= \int_0^n nv^t \, dt$

$= n\overline{a}_{\overline{n}|}$

(b) $\int_0^n t|\bar{a}_{\overline{n-t}|} \, dt = \int_0^n v^t \left(\frac{1 - v^{n-t}}{\delta} \right) dt$

$$= \int_0^n \frac{v^t - v^n}{\delta} \, dt = \frac{\bar{a}_{\overline{n}|} - nv^n}{\delta} = (\bar{I}\bar{a})_{\overline{n}|}$$

2.3.40 The present value is

$$Av + (A+B)v^2 + (A+2B)v^3 + \cdots (A+(n-1)B)v^n$$

$$= (A-B)(v+v^2+v^3+\cdots v^n) + Bv + 2Bv^2 + 3Bv^3 + \cdots + nBv^n$$

$$= (A-B)a_{\overline{n}|} + B(Ia)_{\overline{n}|}$$

The accumulated value is $(A-B)s_{\overline{n}|} + B(Is)_{\overline{n}|} = As_{\overline{n}|} + B(Is)_{\overline{n-1}|}$

SECTION 2.4

2.4.1 (a) (i) $1000a_{\overline{20}|.12} = 7469.44$

(ii) $\dfrac{1000s_{\overline{20}|.06}}{1+.12s_{\overline{20}|.06}} = 6794.19$

(iii) $1000v_{.12}^{20} \cdot s_{\overline{20}|.06} = 3813.44$

(b) (i) $7469.44 = v_i^{20} \cdot 1000s_{\overline{20}|.06} \rightarrow v_i^{20} = .203053$

$\rightarrow i = .0830$

(ii) $6749.19 = 1000a_{\overline{20}|i} \rightarrow i = .1356$

(iii) $6749.19 = 1000 \cdot v_i^{20} \cdot s_{\overline{20}|.06} \rightarrow v_i^{20} = .18347374$

2.4.2 If $i < j$ then $s_{\overline{n}|j} > s_{\overline{n}|i}$, and $a_{\overline{n}|j} < a_{\overline{n}|i}$ so that

$$(1+i')^n = \frac{s_{\overline{n}|j}}{a_{\overline{n}|i}} > \frac{s_{\overline{n}|i}}{a_{\overline{n}|i}} = (1+i)^n \text{ and}$$

$$(1+i')^n = \frac{s_{\overline{n}|j}}{a_{\overline{n}|i}} < \frac{s_{\overline{n}|j}}{a_{\overline{n}|j}} = (1+j)^n. \text{ Thus, } i < i' < j.$$

2.4.3 $\qquad P_1 = K \cdot a_{\overline{n}|}, \ P_2 = \dfrac{K \cdot s_{\overline{n}|j}}{1 + i \cdot s_{\overline{n}|j}} = \dfrac{K}{i}\left[1 - \dfrac{1}{1 + i \cdot s_{\overline{n}|j}}\right]$

$$\frac{1}{P_1} = \frac{1}{K}\left[\frac{1}{s_{\overline{n}|i}} + i\right], \ \frac{1}{P_2} = \frac{1}{K}\left[\frac{1}{s_{\overline{n}|j}} + i\right]$$

The result follows from the fact that

$$s_{\overline{n}|i} = s_{\overline{n}|j} \text{ if } i = j, \ s_{\overline{n}|i} > s_{\overline{n}|j} \text{ if } i > j, \text{ and } s_{\overline{n}|i} < s_{\overline{n}|j} \text{ if } i < j.$$

2.4.4 (a) $(15{,}000 - .10P)s_{\overline{8}|.07} + 10{,}000 = P \ \rightarrow \ P = 80{,}898$

(b) $(15{,}000 - 8500)s_{\overline{8}|.07} + S = 85{,}000 \ \rightarrow \ S = 18{,}311$

2.4.5 $\qquad P_2 = \dfrac{s_{\overline{n}|j}}{1 + i \cdot s_{\overline{n}|j}} = \dfrac{1}{i}\left[1 - \dfrac{1}{1 + i \cdot s_{\overline{n}|j}}\right].$

As j increases, $s_{\overline{n}|j}$ increases, and thus $\dfrac{1}{1 + i \cdot s_{\overline{n}|j}}$ decreases,

and thus $1 - \dfrac{1}{1 + i \cdot s_{\overline{n}|j}}$ increases, showing that $\frac{d}{dj}P_2 > 0$.

2.4.6 If $j < i$ then $(Is)_{\overline{n-1}|j} < (Is)_{\overline{n-1}|i}$, so that

$$s_{\overline{n}|i'} = n + i \cdot (Is)_{\overline{n-1}|j} \ < \ n + i \cdot (Is)_{\overline{n-1}|i}$$

$$= n + \ddot{s}_{\overline{n-1}|i} - (n-1) = s_{\overline{n}|i}$$

$\rightarrow i' < i$, and $s_{\overline{n}|i'} = n + i \cdot (Is)_{\overline{n-1}|j} > n + j \cdot (Is)_{\overline{n-1}|j} = s_{\overline{n}|j}$

$\rightarrow i' > j$.

2.4.7 $(R - 12{,}250)s_{\overline{18}|.035} = 245{,}000 \ \rightarrow \ R = 22{,}250$

2.4.8 (a) $1000(Ia)_{\overline{20}|.10} = 63,920$

(b) $1000(Is)_{\overline{20}|.06} - .10P \cdot s_{\overline{20}|.06} = P \rightarrow P = 67,659$

(c) $P_0(1.10)^t - 1000(Is)_{\overline{t}|.10} = P_t$, until $.10P_{t-1} \le 1000t$

$1000t \cdot s_{\overline{20-t}|.06} + 1000(Is)_{\overline{20-t}|.06} - .10P_t \cdot s_{\overline{20-t}|.06} = P_t$

Solve for t by trial and error.

$t = 8: \rightarrow P_8 = 86,712 \rightarrow P_0 = 61,815, P_1 = 66,997,$
$P_2 = 71,698, P_3 = 75,866, P_4 = 79,453,$
$P_5 = 82,398, P_6 = 84,638, P_7 = 86,102$

2.4.9 Machine I: $X(1-d)^{10} = \frac{X}{8} \rightarrow 1-d = (.125)^{.1}$

First seven years depreciation equals

$A - B_7 = X - X(1-d)^7 = X\left[1 - (.125)^{.7}\right] = .7667X.$

Machine II: First seven years depreciation equals

$A - B_7 = A - \left[S + \left(\frac{1+2+3}{1+2+\cdots+10}\right)(A-S)\right]$

$= Y - \left[\frac{X}{8} + \left(\frac{6}{55}\right)\left(Y - \frac{X}{8}\right)\right] = \left(\frac{49}{55}\right)\left(Y - \frac{X}{8}\right).$

Setting these equal for machines I and II we get

$.7667X = \left(\frac{49}{55}\right)\left(Y - \frac{X}{8}\right) \rightarrow .986X = Y.$

2.4.10 (i) $\frac{X-Y}{n} = 1000$

(ii) $\frac{n-3+1}{S_n}(X-Y) = \frac{n-2}{n(n+1)/2}(X-Y) = 800$

(iii) $Y = (.66875)^n X.$

From (i), and (ii) $\frac{2(n-2)}{n+2} = .8 \rightarrow n = 4$ and $X-Y = 4000.$

From (iii), $X - 4000 = (.66875)^4 X \rightarrow X = 5000.$

2.4.11   Annual deposits at the end of each year for the 15 years are
$.2(20,000)$, $.2(20,000)(.8)$, $.2(20,000)(.8)^2,\ldots,$ $.2(20,000)(.8)^{14.}$

Accumulated value at effective annual 6% is

$$.2(20,000)(1.06)^{14} + .2(20,000(.8)(1.06) \cdot 13$$

$$+ .2(20,000)(.8)(1.06)^{12} + \cdots + .2(20,000)(.8)$$

$$= 4000(1.06)^{14} \left[1 + .8v + (.8)^2 v^2 + \cdots + (.8)^{14} v^{14} \right]$$

$$= 4000(1.06)^{14} \left[\frac{1 - (.8)^{15} v^{15}}{1 - .8v} \right] = 36,329.$$

2.4.12   Under the sum-of-years-digits method, the depreciated value at the end of 4 years in a 10-year depreciation schedule is

$$B_4 = S + \left(\frac{S_{10-4}}{S_{10}} \right)(A-S) = S + \left(\frac{21}{55} \right)(5000-S)$$

$$= 1909.09 + .6182S$$

$$= 2218.$$

We can solve for S, $S = 500$.

Under the straight line method for the remaining 6 years (from time 4 to time 10), the depreciation per year will be

$$\frac{2218 - 500}{6} = 286.3.$$

CHAPTER 3

SECTION 3.1

3.1.1   (i) $L = 1000a_{\overline{5}|.1} + 500v^5 a_{\overline{5}|.1} = 4,967.68$

       (ii) $OB_3 = 4967.68(1.1)^3 - 1000s_{\overline{3}|.1} = 3,301.98$

       (iii) $I_4 = 3301.98(.1) = 330.20,$
             $PR_4 = 1000 - 330.20 = 669.80$

       (iv) $OB_8 = 500a_{\overline{2}|.1} = 867.77$

3.1.2   60 monthly payments. Final 20 payments $(41^{st}, 42^{nd}, \dots)$ are

$$1000(.98)^{40}, 1000(.98)^{41}, \dots, 1000(.98)^{59}.$$

$$
\begin{aligned}
OB_{40} &= 1000(.98)^{40} v_{.0075} + 1000(.98)^{41} v_{.0075}^2 \\
&\qquad\qquad + \cdots + 1000(.98)^{59} v_{.0075}^{20} \\
&= 1000(.98)^{40} v_{.0075} \left[1 + (.98)v + (.98)^2 v^2 + \cdots + (.98)^{19} v^{19} \right] \\
&= 1000(.98)^{40} v_{.0075} \cdot \frac{1 - (.98v)^{20}}{1 - .98v} = 6889.
\end{aligned}
$$

3.1.3 $PV = 250a_{\overline{12}|} + 5(Da)_{\overline{12}|} = 2643.84 + 356.16 = 3000$

3.1.4 (i) With a payment of K per month, the present value of the payments is

$$Ka_{\overline{12}|0} + Kv_0^{12}a_{\overline{36}|.005} = 12K + Ka_{\overline{36}|.005} = 44.8710K.$$

The payment amount is $\dfrac{20,000}{44.8710} = 445.72.$

The outstanding balance at the end of the first year is:

Respectively: $20,000(1+0)^{12} - 445.72s_{\overline{12}|0} = 14,651,$

Prospectively: $445.72a_{\overline{36}|.005} = 14,651.$

(ii) With a payment of C per month, the present value of the payments is

$$Ca_{\overline{12}|.0025} + Cv_{.0025}^{12}a_{\overline{36}|.05/12} = 44.1881K.$$

Note that we formulate the present value of the payments in the usual way an annuity is formulated which has an interest that changes during the term of the annuity.

The payment amount is $\dfrac{20,000}{44.1881} = 452.61.$

The outstanding balance at the end of the first year is:

Respectively: $20,000(1.0025)^{12} - 452.61s_{\overline{12}|.0025} = 15,102,$

Prospectively: $452.61a_{\overline{36}|.05/12} = 15,102.$

3.1.5 Betty will pay $\frac{19,800}{36} = 550$ in principal each month. Her interest payments are $(19,800)(.01) = 198$ at the end of the first month, along with a principal payment of 550, leaving an outstanding balance of 19,250 at the end of the first month. Then she pays $(19,250)(.01) = 192.50$ in interest, and 550 in principal at the end of the second month, leaving an outstanding balance of 18,700 at the end of the second month.

The outstanding balances and interest payments follow the pattern

OB:	19,800	19,250	18,700	18,150	17,600	17,050	. . .
Int.		198	192.50	187	181.50	176	. . .
Prin.		550	550	550	550	550	

After the 16th payment, the remaining schedule of payments is

Int.	110	104.50	99	93.50	88	. . .	11	5.50
Prin.	550		550	550	550	550	550	550

This is what Bank Y purchases. Bank Y has monthly rate of interest j, where $(1+j)^6 = 1.07$, so that $j = .01134$. The price paid by Bank Y for the remaining payments after the 16th is

$$5.5(Da)_{\overline{20}|j} + 550a_{\overline{20}|j} = 10,857.3.$$

3.1.6
$$\begin{aligned}
L = OB_0 &= (OB_0 - OB_1) + (OB_1 - OB_2) + \cdots + (OB_{n-1} - OB_n) \\
&= PR_1 + PR_2 + \cdots + PR_n \\
&= (K_1 - I_1) + (K_2 - I_2) + \cdots + (K_n - I_n) = K_T - I_T
\end{aligned}$$

3.1.7 $OB_{t+1} = OB_t \cdot (1+i) - K_{t+1}$ and $OB_t = OB_{t-1} \cdot (1+i) - K_t$

$$\rightarrow OB_t - OB_{t+1} = (OB_{t-1} - OB_t)(1+i) - (K_t - K_{t+1})$$

$$\rightarrow PR_{t+1} = PR_t \cdot (1+i) + K_{t+1} - K_t$$

3.1.8 $L = 595a_{\overline{120}|.01} + 5(Ia)_{\overline{120}|.01} = 58,490.89.$

$PR_1 = 600 - (.01)(58,490.89) = 15.09.$ From 3.1.7 we have

$PR_{t+1} = PR_t \cdot (1.01) + 5 \rightarrow PR_2 = PR_1 \cdot (1.01) + 5,$

$PR_3 = PR_1 \cdot (1.01)^2 + 5(1.01) + 5 = PR_1 \cdot (1.01)^2 + 5s_{\overline{2}|},\dots,$

$PR_t = PR_1 \cdot (1.01)^{t-1} + 5s_{\overline{t-1}|}.$

Prospectively, $OB_{60} = 595a_{\overline{60}|.01} + 5(Ia)_{\overline{60}|} = 46,424$

Retrospectively, $OB_{60} = 58,490.89(1.01)^{60} - 595s_{\overline{60}|} - 5(Is)_{\overline{60}|}$

$\sum_{k=1}^{60} PR_k = \sum_{k=1}^{60}\left[15.09(1.01)^{k-1} + 5s_{\overline{k-1}|}\right] = 15.09s_{\overline{60}|} + 5(Is)_{\overline{59}|}$

$I_{61} = OB_{60} \cdot (.01) = 464.24,$

$PR_{61} = 15.09(1.01)^{60} + 5s_{\overline{60}|} = 435.76$

$PR_{61} = K_{61} - I_{61} = 900 - 464.24 = 435.76$

3.1.9   During the first 10 years, interest only is paid. Therefore, after each interest payment, the outstanding balance remains unchanged at 1000. At the end of 10 years the outstanding balance is still 1000. To see what happens during the second 10 years we consider a general situation with a loan of amount L at annual interest rate i and annual payments equal to $(1.5)\times$ Interest due. The interest due is equal to the previous outstanding balance multiplied by the interest rate. The schedule of payments is as follows:

Time t	10	11	12	13	14 $\cdots$
OB_t	L	$L(1-.5i)$	$L(1-.5i)^2$	$L(1-.5i)^3$	$L(1-.5i)^4$
I_t		Li	$L(1-.5i)i$	$L(1-.5i)^2 i$	
K_t		$1.5\,Li$	$1.5L(1-.5i)i$	$1.5L(1-.5i)^2 i$	
PR_t		$.5\,Li$	$L(1-.5i)(.5i)$	$L(1-.5i)^2(.5i)$	
OB_t		$L-.5Li$	$L(1-.5i)^2$	$L(1-.5i)^3$	

We see that the principal repaid in a particular payment is always $.5i$ multiplied by the previous outstanding balance, and therefore, the new outstanding balance is $1-.5i$ multiplied by the previous outstanding balance. As long as the payments follow the pattern of $(1.5)\times$ Interest due, the successive outstanding balances will form the geometric series given in the top line of the table above. The factor ".5" could be changed and a similar pattern would occur. For instance, if we had been told that each payment is 125% of the amount of interest due then the successive outstanding balances would form the geometric series

$$L, \ L(1-.25i), \ L(1-.25i)^2, \ L(1-.25i)^3, L(1-.25i)^4,\dots \ .$$

In this example, we have noted above that the balance at the end of 10 years is still 1000. Then during the second 10 years the payments are $(1.5) \times$ Interest due. With interest rate $i=.10$, we get $.5i=.05$, and the successive outstanding balances form the geometric series

$$1000 \ (\text{at time } 10), \ 1000(1-.05)(\text{time } 11), 1000(1-.05)^2 \ (\text{time } 12)\cdots$$
$$\cdots 1000(1-.05)^{10} \ = 598.74 \ (\text{time } 20).$$

For the final 10 years, the payment is X, so the outstanding balance of 598.74 at time 20 must be equal to $Xa_{\overline{10}|.1}$ (prospective form of outstanding balance).

Therefore, $Xa_{\overline{10}|.1} \ = 598.74 \ \rightarrow \ X \ = 97.44.$

3.1.10 $L \cdot v_i^n + L \cdot i \cdot a_{\overline{n}|i} \ = L$

3.1.11   (a) $1000 = K\left[2a_{\overline{144}|.01} - a_{\overline{72}|.01}\right] \ \rightarrow \ K = 9.89(9.888857)$

        (b) $PR_1 \ = 9.89 - 10 \ = -.11, \ OB_{1\,mo} \ = 1000.11,$

           $OB_{2\,mo} \ = 1000.22,\dots,$

           $OB_{12\,mo} \ = 1001.41, \ OB_t \ = 1000 + .11s_{\overline{t}|}$

3.1.12 (a)   Example 3.1

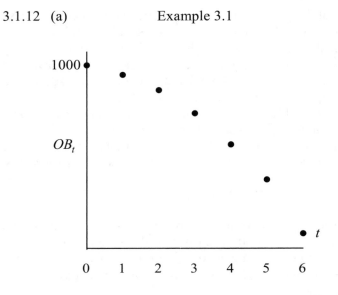

Example 3.2

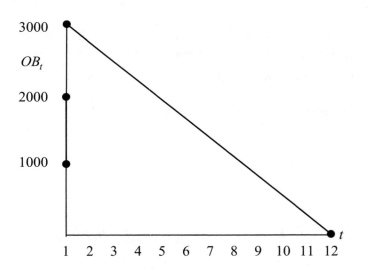

3.1.13 (b) $PR_6 = K_6 - OB_5 \cdot i = 500 - \left[1000a_{\overline{10}|} - a_{\overline{1}|}\right] \cdot i$

$$= 500\left[1 - i(2a_{\overline{10}|} - v)\right]$$

(a) From (b), $PR_6 = 500\left[1 - 2(1 - v^{10}) + (1 - v)\right] = 500(2v^{10} - v)$

(c) Since the first 6 payments are level, $PR_6 = PR_1 \cdot (1+i)^5$, but $PR_1 = 500 - L \cdot i$.

SECTION 3.2

3.2.1 $L = K \cdot a_{\overline{n}|i} \;\rightarrow\; L(1+i)^t = K \cdot a_{\overline{n}|i} \cdot (1+i)^t = K\left[s_{\overline{t}|} + a_{\overline{n-t}|i}\right]$

$OB_t = L(1+i)^t - K \cdot s_{\overline{t}|} = L + L \cdot i \cdot s_{\overline{t}|} - K \cdot s_{\overline{t}|}$

$$= L - (K - L \cdot i)s_{\overline{t}|} = L - PR_t \cdot s_{\overline{t}|}$$

3.2.2 Quarterly payment is $\dfrac{3000}{a_{\overline{12}|.02}} = 283.68$, so that total interest paid is $12(283.68) - 3000 = 404.15$. The original payment scheme has larger payments earlier, reducing the OB more quickly, and therefore reducing the amounts of interest paid.

3.2.3 $OB_0 - 156.00 = 706.00 \;\rightarrow\; OB_0 = 862.00,$

$43.10 = I_1 = OB_0 \cdot i = 862.00 \cdot i \;\rightarrow\; i = .05$

$K = I_1 + PR_1 = 199.10$

Year (t)	OB_t	I_t	PR_t
0	862.00		
1	706.00	43.10	156.00
2	542.20	35.30	163.80
3	370.21	27.11	171.99
4	189.62	18.51	180.59
5	0	9.48	189.62

3.2.4 $OB_0 = a_{\overline{60}|.01} = 44.9514,\ OB_t = a_{\overline{60-t}|.01}$ at t months

$\rightarrow\ 22.4757 = a_{\overline{60-t}|.01} = \dfrac{1-v^{60-t}}{.01}\ \rightarrow\ t = 34.4.$

$OB_{34} = 22.795 > 22.4757 > 22.023 = OB_{35}.$

$t = 35$ is June 1, 2007.

3.2.5   (a) Let j be the 6-month effective rate of interest. Then

   $PR_1 = 156.24 = Kv_j^{10}$

   $\rightarrow\ v_j^{10} = .7812\ \rightarrow\ j = .025$

   $\rightarrow\ i^{(12)} = 12\left[(1+j)^{1/6} - 1\right] = .0495.$

   (b) Let j be the monthly effective interest rate. The principal repaid in the first 12 payments is $2400 - 983.16 = 1416.84$

   $\rightarrow\ 2215.86 = 1416.84(1+j)^{36}$

   $\rightarrow\ j = .0125\ \rightarrow\ i^{(12)} = .15.$

3.2.6   (a) $(K - 103)(1.08) = K - 98\ \rightarrow\ K = 165.50$ is   the   level
   payment $\rightarrow\ PR_{Feb\,05} = 67.50$

   (b) $OB_{Feb\,03} = \dfrac{103.00}{.08} = 1287.50 = 165.50a_{\overline{n}|.08}\ \rightarrow\ n = 12.7.$
   Thus there are 12 regular payments and a final smaller 13th
   payment of February 1, 2016 of amount X, where
   $1287.50 = 165.50a_{\overline{12}|} + X \cdot v^{13}\ \rightarrow\ X = 109.54.$

3.2.7 $X(1.06)^{10} - X = 356.54 + 10P - X$ and $P = \dfrac{X}{a_{\overline{10}|.06}}$

   $\rightarrow\ X(1.06)^{10} - X = 356.54 + \dfrac{10X}{a_{\overline{10}|.06}} - X\ \rightarrow\ X = 825.$

3.2.8   (i) $K = \dfrac{2000}{a_{\overline{10}|.0807}} = 299.00 \;\rightarrow\;$ total paid $= 2990.$

     (ii) Payments are
$$200 + 2000i,\; 200 + 1800i,\; 200 + 1600i, \ldots, 200 + 200i.$$
Total paid is
$$2000 + 200i(10+9+\cdots+1) \;=\; 2000 + 200i \cdot \frac{10(11)}{2} \;=\; 2990$$
$$\rightarrow \; i = .09.$$

3.2.9   Suppose the payment is 1 per month.
$$OB_{5\,yr} = a_{\overline{120}|.01} = 69.70052.$$

With penalty, the new OB becomes
$$(1+.01k)(69.70052).$$

This is amortized for 10 years with monthly payments at $i^{(12)} = .09$ for a monthly payment of
$$\frac{(1+.01k)(69.70052)}{a_{\overline{120}|.0075}} = (1+.01k)(.882937).$$

Her decision to refinance is correct if new payment does not exceed old payment $\rightarrow$ $(1+.01k)(.882937) \leq 1 \;\rightarrow\; k \leq .1326.$

3.2.10   (a) 3.1:   Present value of interest:
$$10 \cdot v_{.01} + 8.94 \cdot v^2 + \cdots + 2.29 \cdot v^6 \;=\; 39.33$$

                     Present value of principal:
$$105.61 \cdot v + \cdots + 228.93 \cdot v^6$$
$$= 1000 - present\ value\ of\ interest \;=\; 960.67$$

         3.4:   Present value of interest:
$$5(Da)_{\overline{12}|.02} \;=\; 356.16$$

                     Present value of principal:
$$250a_{\overline{12}|} \;=\; 3000 - present\ value\ of\ interest$$
$$= 2643.84$$

(b) Payment amount is $K = \dfrac{L}{a_{\overline{n}|}}$ and $I_t = K(1 - v^{n-t+1})$

Present value of interest:

$$\sum_{t=1}^{n} K(1 - v^{n-t+1}) \cdot v^t = \frac{L}{a_{\overline{n}|}} \cdot \sum_{t=1}^{n} (v^t - v^{n+1}) = L\left[1 - \frac{nv^{n+1}}{a_{\overline{n}|}}\right]$$

Present value of principal:

$$\sum_{t=1}^{n} K \cdot v^{n-t+1} \cdot v^t = L \cdot \frac{nv^{n+1}}{a_{\overline{n}|}} = L - \text{present value of interest}$$

3.2.11 $PR_t = 5190.72 - 5084.68 = 106.04$, and $PR_{t+1} = 111.02$

$\rightarrow \; 1 + j = \dfrac{111.02}{106.04} = 1.046963$

$I_t = (5190.72)(.046963) = 243.77 \;\rightarrow\; K = I_t + PR_t = 349.81$

3.2.12   At $i^{(12)} = .12$, the house buyer will have a monthly payment of $\dfrac{100,000}{a_{\overline{300}|.01}} = 1053.22$ for three years, and then will have

$$OB_{3 \; yrs} = 97,707.45.$$

When Smith sells the loan to the broker which values payments at $i^{(12)} = .15$, Smith receives

$$97,707.45 v_{.0125}^{36} + 1053.22 a_{\overline{36}|.0125} = 92,858.$$

Smith receives 192,858 in total.

3.2.13 (i) Payment amount is $\frac{L}{a_{\overline{n}|i}}$. Total interest paid is $n \cdot \frac{L}{a_{\overline{n}|i}} - L$.

(ii) Total interest paid is

$$L \cdot i\left[1 + \frac{n-1}{n} + \frac{n-2}{n} + \cdots + \frac{2}{n} + \frac{1}{n}\right] = L \cdot i \cdot \frac{n+1}{2}.$$

Under Scheme (i) $OB_t = \frac{L}{a_{\overline{n}|}} \cdot a_{\overline{n-t}|}$ and under Scheme (ii),

$OB_t = \frac{L}{n}(n-t)$. Since $\frac{d^2}{dt^2} a_{\overline{n-t}|} = -\delta^2 \cdot v^{n-t} < 0$ and

$\frac{d^2}{dt^2}(n-t) = 0$, and since $OB_0 = L$ for both schemes and

$OB_n = 0$ for both schemes, it follows that $OB_t^{(i)} > OB_t^{(ii)}$ for

$0 < t < n$, since $OB_t^{(i)}$ is a concave function of t. Thus,

$I_t^{(i)} \geq I_t^{(ii)}$ (with $>$ for $0 < t < n$), and $I_T^{(i)} \geq I_T^{(ii)}$ (with $>$ if

$i > 0$ and $n > 1$). The payments under scheme (ii) can be

split into n level payments of $\frac{L}{n}$ each plus a decreasing

series of interest payments of amounts

$$\frac{L}{n}\left[n + (n-1) + (n-2) + \cdots + 2 + 1\right] \cdot i.$$

The present value at interest rate i is

$$\frac{L}{n} \cdot a_{\overline{n}|} + \frac{L \cdot i}{n} \cdot (Da)_{\overline{n}|} = \frac{L}{n} \cdot a_{\overline{n}|} + \frac{L \cdot i}{n} \cdot \frac{n - a_{\overline{n}|}}{i} = L.$$

3.2.14 A: $125{,}000 a_{\overline{5}|} = 541{,}184.58$

B: $75{,}000 a_{\overline{5}|} = 324{,}710.75$

C: $10{,}000(Da)_{\overline{5}|} = 134{,}104.67$

3.2.15 (a) $OB_1 = 1000(1.01) - 100 = 910, I_1 = 10, PR_1 = 90$

$OB_2 = 910(1.01) - 100 = 819.10, \ I_2 = 9.1, \ PR_2 = 90.90, \ldots,$

$OB_{10} = 58.40,$ and the smaller payment necessary at time 11 is $58.40(1.01) = 58.98.$ Alternatively,

$$1000 = 100a_{\overline{n}|} \quad \rightarrow \quad a_{\overline{n}|} = 10$$

$$\rightarrow \quad n = \frac{\ln\left[1 - 10(.01)\right]}{\ln(v)} = 10.59.$$

This indicates that 10 full payments plus a fractional payment are needed. If that fractional payment is X at time 11, then $1000 = 100a_{\overline{10}|} + X \cdot v^{11} \quad \rightarrow \quad X = 58.98.$

3.2.16 (a) (i) Annual payment is $K = \dfrac{L}{a_{\overline{n}|i}} = \dfrac{L \cdot i}{1 - v_i^n}$

(ii) Monthly payment is $J = \dfrac{L}{a_{\overline{12n}|j}} = \dfrac{L \cdot j}{1 - v_j^{12n}},$

where $(1+j)^{12} = 1+i,$ so that $v_j^{12n} = v_i^n.$

$$OB_t^{(i)} = L \cdot \frac{a_{\overline{n-t}|i}}{a_{\overline{n}|i}} = L \cdot \frac{1 - v_i^{n-t}}{1 - v_i^n}$$

$$OB_t^{(ii)} = L \cdot \frac{a_{\overline{12(n-t)}|j}}{a_{\overline{12n}|j}} = L \cdot \frac{1 - v_j^{12(n-t)}}{1 - v_j^{12n}}$$

$$= L \cdot \frac{1 - v_i^{n-t}}{1 - v_i^n} = OB_t^{(i)}$$

(b) Total paid in Scheme (i) is $n \cdot K,$ and under Scheme (ii) is $12n \cdot J.$ Since $\dfrac{K}{J} = \dfrac{i}{j},$ and since $j = \dfrac{i^{(12)}}{12} \leq \dfrac{i}{12},$ it follows that $K \geq 12J$ so that $n \cdot K \geq 12n \cdot J.$

3.2.17 $OB_n = a_{\overline{n}|} = \frac{3}{4} \cdot a_{\overline{2n}|} \rightarrow 1 - v^n = \frac{3}{4}(1 - v^{2n})$

$\rightarrow 1 + v^n = \frac{4}{3} \rightarrow v^n = \frac{1}{3}$

Principal in the $(n+1)^{st}$ payment is $v^{2n-(n+1)+1} = v^n = \frac{1}{3}$

Interest in the $(n+1)^{st}$ payment is $\frac{2}{3}$

3.2.18 Monthly payment is $K = \dfrac{1000}{a_{\overline{18}|.0075} + v^{18}_{.0075} \cdot a_{\overline{6}|.01}} = 45.7764$

$I_{1st\ mo} = 1000(.0075) = 7.50, \quad PR_{1st\ mo} = 45.78 - 7.50 = 38.28,$

$OB_{1\ mo} = 961.72, \ldots, OB_{12\ mo} = K\left[a_{\overline{6}|.0075} + v^6_{.0075} \cdot a_{\overline{6}|.01}\right] = 521.26$

$\rightarrow$ principal repaid in the first year is

$$OB_0 - OB_{12\ mo} = 478.74$$

3.2.19 (i) $K = \dfrac{75,000}{a_{\overline{300}|.01}} = 789.92.$ Total paid is $300K = 236,976;$

total interest is $236,976 - 75,000 = 161,976.$

(ii) $75,000 = 789.92[v + v^2 + v^3 + v^4 + v^5 + 2v^6$

$+ v^7 + v^8 + v^9 + v^{10} + v^{11} + 2v^{12} + \cdots]$

$= 789.92[v + v^2 + v^3 + v^4 + v^5 + 2v^6][1 + v^6 + v^{12} + \cdots]$

Let $j = (1.01)^6 - 1$, so that $v_j = v^6_{.01}$

$\rightarrow 75,000 = 789.92\left[a_{\overline{6}|.01} + v^6_{.01}\right] \cdot \ddot{a}_{\overline{n}|j}$

$\rightarrow \ddot{a}_{\overline{n}|j} = 14.0922$

$\rightarrow n = 28.4,$ where n counts half-years.

After 14 years (just after the payment on July 1, 2019), the outstanding balance is

$$75,000(1.01)^{168} - 789.92\left[a_{\overline{6}|.01} + v_{.01}^6\right] \cdot \ddot{s}_{\overline{28}|j} = 2269.34.$$

$OB_{8/1/19} = 2269.34(1.01) - 789.92 = 1502.12$, and
$OB_{9/1/19} = 1502.12(1.01) - 789.22 = 727.22$, so the final smaller payment on October 1, 2019 is $727.22(1.01) = 734.49$. Total paid is $28(7K) + 2K + 734.49 = 157,139$, and the total interest is 82,139.

(iii) OB's are 75,000, 74,750, 74,500, 74,250
Interest payments are 750, 747.50, 745, 742.50,..., for a total of $2.50[300 + 299 + 298 + \cdots + 1] = 112,875$

3.2.20 $OB_4 = p \cdot a_{\overline{n-4}|} = v^2 \cdot 1.16 p \cdot a_{\overline{n-6}|} \rightarrow (1-v^{n-4})$

$$= 1.16 \cdot v^2 \cdot (1-v^{n-6})$$

With $i = .05$, this results in $.194481v^n = .052154 \rightarrow n = 27$.
Alternatively, the accumulated value of the missed payments at time 5 is $p \cdot s_{\overline{2}|}$. This must be recovered in the extra $.16p$ in each of the remaining $n-6$ payments. Thus, $p \cdot s_{\overline{2}|} = .16 p \cdot a_{\overline{n-6}|}$.

3.2.21 At time t the OB_t can be regarded as a "new" loan with $n-t$ remaining payments of K each. The retrospective OB u periods later is $L^{new} \cdot (1+i)^u - K \cdot s_{\overline{u}|} = OB_t \cdot (1+i)^u - K \cdot s_{\overline{u}|}$. In general,

$$OB_{t+u} = OB_t \cdot (1+i)^u - \left[K_{t+1} \cdot (1+i)^{u-1}\right.$$

$$\left. + K_{t+2} \cdot (1+i)^{u-2} + \cdots + K_u\right]$$

3.2.22 $K \cdot a_{\overline{15}|} = OB_5 = v^3 \cdot (K+X) \cdot a_{\overline{12}|}$

$\rightarrow$ $X = (1+i)^3 \cdot \dfrac{K}{a_{\overline{12}|}} \cdot \left(a_{\overline{15}|} - v^3 \cdot a_{\overline{12}|}\right) = K \cdot \dfrac{s_{\overline{3}|}}{a_{\overline{12}|}}$

Difference in interest is the total additional payment made:

$$K\left[\frac{12s_{\overline{3}|}}{a_{\overline{12}|}} - 3\right]$$

3.2.23 $i^{(12)} = .06$: Monthly payment is $\dfrac{100,000}{a_{\overline{300}|.005}} = 644.30$

(more precisely, 644.301402)

Total interest over 25 years is 93,290.

The one week interest rate is

$j = \left((1.005)^{12}\right)^{7/365} - 1 = .001148477$

(i) $B_1 = 161.08 \rightarrow 100,000 = 161.08 a_{\overline{n}|j}$

$\rightarrow$ $n = 1087.5$ weeks (just under 21 years)

$\rightarrow$ $100,000 = 161.08 a_{\overline{1087}|j} + X \cdot v_j^{1088}$

$\rightarrow$ $X = 76.40$

$\rightarrow$ total paid 175,170 $\rightarrow$ total interest $= 75,170$

(ii) $B_2 = 148.68(148.6849388) \rightarrow n = 1289.7$
(just under 25 years)

$\rightarrow$ $100,000 = 148.68 \cdot a_{\overline{1289}|j} + X \cdot v_j^{1290} \rightarrow X = 109.21$

$\rightarrow$ total paid $= 191,758 \rightarrow$ total interest $= 91,758$

At an interest rate of $i^{(12)} = .24$, the monthly payment is 2005.27, and total interest over 25 years is 501,581. The one week interest rate is $\left((1.02)^{12}\right)^{7/365} - 1 = .004567717$.

(i) $B_1 = 501.32$, $n = 531.2$ (just over 10 years), $X = 81$, total interest $= 166,282$

(ii) $B_2 = 462.75$, $n = 954.3$ (just over 18 years), $X = 139$, total interest $= 341,604$

3.2.24 (a) $OB_t = L \cdot \dfrac{n-t}{n}$, $\quad I_t = OB_{t-1} \cdot i = L \cdot \dfrac{n-t+1}{n} \cdot i$, $\quad PR_t = \dfrac{L}{n}$,

and $K_{t.} = \dfrac{L}{n} + L \cdot \dfrac{n-t+1}{n} \cdot i$. Then

$$PR_k = PR_{k-1} \cdot (1+i) + K_k - K_{k-1}$$

$$= \frac{L}{n}(1+i) + \frac{L}{n} + L \cdot \frac{n-t+1}{n} \cdot i$$

$$- \left[\frac{L}{n} + L \cdot \frac{n-(k-1)+1}{n} \cdot i \right] = \frac{L}{n}.$$

(b) $L = \displaystyle\sum_{t=1}^{n} \left[\frac{L}{n} + L \cdot \frac{n-t+1}{n} \cdot i \right] \cdot v^t \; \rightarrow \; n = \sum_{t=1}^{n} [1 + (n-t+1) \cdot i] \cdot v^t$

Consider a bank account with initial deposit n, and withdrawals of amount 1 each for n years. The successive yearly interest amounts generated in the account will be $n \cdot i$, $(n-1) \cdot i, \ldots, 2i, i$. Thus, the initial deposit n is the present value of the withdrawals and interest payments it generates.

(c) $\displaystyle\sum_{t=1}^{n} [1 + (n-t) \cdot d] \cdot v^{t-1} = \ddot{a}_{\overline{n}|} + d \cdot (D\ddot{a})_{\overline{n-1}|}$

$$= \ddot{a}_{\overline{n}|} + (n-1) - a_{\overline{n-1}|} = n$$

3.2.25 $OB_t = L(1+i)^t - K \cdot \overline{s}_{\overline{t}|i}$, where $K = \dfrac{L}{a_{\overline{n}|i}}$. Then

$$\frac{d}{dt}OB_t = \frac{d}{dt}\left[L \cdot e^{\delta t} - K\int_0^t (1+i)^s\, ds\right]$$
$$= L(1+i)^t \cdot \delta - K(1+i)^t$$

Also $\dfrac{d}{dt}OB_t = \dfrac{d}{dt}K\displaystyle\int_0^{n-t} v^s\, ds = -K \cdot v^{n-t}$.

Rate at which principal is being repaid at time t is $-\dfrac{d}{dt}OB_t$. Rate at which interest is being paid at time t is K minus the rate at which principal is being repaid at time t.

$$PR_{t \to t+1} = OB_t - OB_{t+1} = K \cdot \overline{a}_{\overline{n-t}|} - K \cdot \overline{a}_{\overline{n-t-1}|} = K \cdot v^{n-t} \cdot \frac{i}{\delta}, \quad \text{and}$$
$$I_{t \to t+1} = K - PR_{t \to t+1}, \frac{d^2}{dt^2}OB_t = K \cdot \frac{d}{dt}(-v^{n-t}) = -K \cdot \delta \cdot v^{n-t}$$

3.2.26 $OB_{n-1} = X - 6009.12 \;\to\; I_n = OB_{n-1} \cdot i$

$$= (X - 6009.12)(.125) = 153.86$$

$\to\; X = 7240$.

Also, $I_n = K(1-v)$, where K is the level payment

$\to\; 153.86 = K\left(1 - \dfrac{1}{1.25}\right) \;\to\; K = 1384.74$. Then

$I_1 = X \cdot i = (7240)(.125) = 905$

$\to\; PR_1 = K - I_1 = 1384.74 - 905 = 479.74$

3.2.27 (a) $L = K \cdot a_{\overline{n-1}|} + B \cdot v^n \quad \rightarrow \quad I_1 = OB_0 \cdot i$

$$= K \cdot i = K(1 - v^{n-1}) + B \cdot v^n \cdot i$$

$\rightarrow$ (since $i \cdot v = d$)

$$PR_1 = K - I_1 = K \cdot v^{n-1} - B \cdot v^{n-1} \cdot d$$

$$= K \cdot v^n + K(v^{n-1} - v^n) - B \cdot v^{n-1} \cdot d$$

$$= K \cdot v^n + K \cdot v^{n-1} \cdot (1 - v) - B \cdot v^{n-1} \cdot d$$

$$= K \cdot v^n + (K - B) \cdot v^{n-1} \cdot d$$

$\rightarrow \quad PR_t = PR_1 \cdot (1+i)^{t-1} = K \cdot v^{n-t+1} + (K-B) \cdot v^{n-t} \cdot d$

(since PR grows a factor of $1+i$ every period as long as payments are level).

(b) $n = 11$, $B = 58.98$, $K = 100$, $i = .01$

$$\rightarrow \quad PR_1 = 100 v^{11} + (100 - 58.98) \cdot v^{10} \cdot d$$

$$= 89.63 + .37 = 90$$

3.2.28 (a) $OB_t = t \cdot a_{\overline{n-t}|i} + (Ia)_{\overline{n-t}|i}$,

$$I_t = t - 1 - n \cdot v^{n-t+1} + \ddot{a}_{\overline{n-t+1}|i}, \quad PR_t = t - I_t$$

(b) $OB_t = (Da)_{\overline{n-t}|i}$, $I_t = n - t + 1 - a_{\overline{n-t+1}|i}$

$$PR_t = n - t + 1 - I_t$$

3.2.29 (a) $(1+i) \cdot v + (1+i)^2 \cdot v^2 + \cdots + (1+i)^n \cdot v^{n-t} = n$

(b) $OB_t = (1+i)^{t+1} \cdot v + (1+i)^{t+2} \cdot v^2 + \cdots + (1+i)^n \cdot v^{n-t}$

$$= (n-t)(1+i)^t$$

3.2.30 (a) $OB_t = \int_t^n K_s \cdot v^{s-t}\, ds$ (prospective)

$$= L(1+i)^t - \int_0^t K_s \cdot (1+i)^{t-s} \cdot \delta\, ds \quad \text{(retrospective)}$$

$$\frac{d}{dt} OB_t = L(1+i)^t \cdot \delta - K_t - \int_0^t K_s \cdot (1+i)^{t-s} \cdot \delta\, ds$$

$$= OB_t \cdot \delta - K_t$$

(b) $PR_{t_0 \to t_1} = OB_{t_0} - OB_{t_1}, \quad I_{t_0 \to t_1} = \int_t^n K_s\, ds - PR_{t_0 \to t_1}$

3.2.31 (a) $K = \dfrac{10,000}{a_{\overline{20|}}} = 1018.52, \quad PR_6 = 1018.52 v^{20-6+1} = 321.08,$

$PR_7 = 346.77$ and $PR_8 = 374.51$. Before the extra payments
are made, $OB_5 = 1018.52 a_{\overline{15|}} = 8718.02$. After the extra pay-
ments are made, $OB_5' = 7675.66$. This can be paid off in n
more payments of 1018.52, where

$$7675.66 = 1018,52 a_{\overline{n|}} \;\to\; n = \frac{\ln\left[1 - \left(\frac{7675.66}{1018.52}\right)(.08)\right]}{\ln(v)} = 12.$$

The additional 12 payments result in a total of 17 payments,
along with the extra principal payment at $t = 5$.

(b) After the additional payments at time t_0 the new outstanding
balance is $OB_{t_0}' = OB_{t_0} - PR_{t_0+1} - PR_{t_0+2} - \cdots - PR_{t_0+m} = OB_{t_0+m}.$
This new outstanding balance will be paid off with
$n - (t_0+m)$ more payments for a total of $n - m$ payments.

3.2.32 (a) $1000(.12550881)[10+9+\cdots+2+1] = 6902.98$

     (b) $1000(.0609)(2)[10+9+\cdots+2+1] = 6699$

     (c) $1000(.03)(4)[10+9+\cdots+2+1] = 6600$

      Since $.0609s_{\overline{2}|.0609} = .03s_{\overline{4}|.03} = .12550881$, the interest pay-

      ments are all equivalent at $i^{(4)} = .12$.

3.2.33 Given a schedule of principal repayments on a loan of amount L, say $PR_1, PR_2,\ldots,PR_n$, at times $1,2,\ldots,n$, such that $\sum_{t=1}^{n} PR_t = L$, then for any interest rate j,

$$L = \sum_{t=1}^{n}\left[PR_t + I_t\right]\cdot v_j^t = \sum_{t=1}^{n}\left[PR_t + OB_{t-1}\cdot j\right]\cdot v_j^t,$$

where $OB_1 = L - PR_1$, $OB_2 = OB_1 - PR_2,\ldots$.

Suppose we consider the amortization at rate i, based on payments $K_1, K_2,\ldots, K_n$, and record the principal amounts in each payment. Then, using the same principal payments in this amortization, at interest rate $j = i(1-r)$ yields the result (i.e., I_t is now $OB_t \cdot i \cdot (1-r)$, but PR_t is unchanged.)

3.2.34

t	OB	PR	I
0	10,000.00	—	—
1	9,400.00	600.00	900.00
2	8,740.00	660.00	840.00
3	8,014.00	726.00	774.00
4	7,215.40	798.60	701.40
5	6,336.94	878.46	621.54
6	5,370.63	966.31	533.69
7	4,307.69	1062.94	437.06
8	3,152.31	1,155.38	341.62
9	1,904.49	1,247.82	252.18
10	556.85	1,347.64	152.36
11	0	556.85	44.55

3.2.35 This is the same situation as in Problem 3.2.33 where interest was reduced because of tax instead of insurance. Algebraically, the situations are the same.

SECTION 3.3

3.3.1 $(X-12,000) \cdot s_{\overline{10}|.08} + X \cdot s_{\overline{5}|.08} = 100,000 \rightarrow X = 13,454.36$

3.3.2 (a) $16,902.95 = L\left(.10 + \dfrac{1}{s_{\overline{10}|.08}}\right) \rightarrow L = 100,000$

(b) $K = L\left(i + \dfrac{1}{s_{\overline{n}|j}}\right) \rightarrow L = \dfrac{K \cdot s_{\overline{n}|j}}{1 + i \cdot s_{\overline{n}|j}}$

3.3.3 Sinking fund reaches 10,000 with the nth deposit, where

$$10,000 = 100 s_{\overline{n}|.0075} \rightarrow n = 74.9 \rightarrow 10,000 = 100 \ddot{s}_{\overline{74}|.0075} + X$$

$$\rightarrow X = 81.67.$$

Total paid during the course of the loan is

$$10,000(.0125)(75) + 100(74) + 81.67 = 16,856.67.$$

3.3.4 Total annual outlay under option (a) is $\dfrac{250,000}{a_{\overline{30}|.12}} = 31,035.91$.

Total annual outlay under option (b) is

$$250,000\left(.10 + \dfrac{1}{s_{\overline{30}|j}}\right) \rightarrow s_{\overline{30}|j} = 41.418745 \rightarrow j = .021322$$

3.3.5   (a)   With purchase price X, $[16,902.95 - .1X] \cdot s_{\overline{10}|.08} = X$

$\rightarrow \quad X = 100,000$

(b)   Total annual outlay is $L\left(i + \frac{1}{s_{\overline{n}|j}}\right)$. Investor will pay P, where

$$\left(L\left(i + \frac{1}{s_{\overline{n}|j}}\right) - P \cdot i\right) \cdot s_{\overline{n}|j} = P$$

$$\rightarrow \quad L\left(i \cdot s_{\overline{n}|j} + 1\right) = P\left(i \cdot s_{\overline{n}|j} + 1\right) \quad \rightarrow \quad P = L$$

3.3.6   The amortization payment P is the solution of the relationship $1000 = Pa_{\overline{10}|.1}$, so that $P = 162.75$. Under the sinking fund method, with loan interest rate still at 10%, the interest payments at the end of each year are 100, and the sinking fund deposits are $162.75 - 100 = 62.75$. The accumulated value of the sinking fund just before the repayment of the loan is $62.75 s_{\overline{10}|.14} = 1213$, and just after the 1000 loan is repaid, the balance in the sinking fund is 213.

3.3.7   Current monthly profit is $9000(85) - C$, where C is the current monthly cost. New monthly profit is

$$12,000X - C - 15,816 - 1,500,000(.015) - \frac{1,500,000}{s_{\overline{40}|.01}}$$

$$= 9000(85) - C + 30,000 \quad \rightarrow \quad X = 72.00$$

3.3.8 $L\left(i + \frac{1}{s_{\overline{n}|j}}\right) = \frac{L}{a_{\overline{n}|i'}} \quad \rightarrow \quad i + \frac{1}{s_{\overline{n}|j}} = \frac{1}{a_{\overline{n}|i'}}.$

Since $i + \frac{1}{s_{\overline{n}|i}} = \frac{1}{a_{\overline{n}|i}}$ it follows that if $j < i$, then $s_{\overline{n}|j} < s_{\overline{n}|i}$

$$\rightarrow \frac{1}{a_{\overline{n}|i'}} = i + \frac{1}{s_{\overline{n}|j}} > i + \frac{1}{s_{\overline{n}|i}} = \frac{1}{a_{\overline{n}|i}} \quad \rightarrow \quad a_{\overline{n}|i} > a_{\overline{n}|i'} \quad \rightarrow \quad i' > i.$$

The inequalities reverse if $j > i$. Part (a) of Example 3.6 has $i' = .1089$, but according to the approximation,

$$i' = .10 + \tfrac{1}{2}(.02) = .11.$$

3.3.9 $\displaystyle\sum_{t=1}^{n}(K_t - L \cdot i)\cdot(1+j)^{n-t} = L$

$$\rightarrow \; L = \frac{\displaystyle\sum_{t=1}^{n} K_t \cdot (1+j)^{n-t}}{1+i\cdot s_{\overline{n}|j}} = \frac{\displaystyle\sum_{t=1}^{n} K_t \cdot v_j^t}{v_j^n + i\cdot a_{\overline{n}|j}}$$

$Y = v_j^n + i\cdot a_{\overline{n}|j}$

3.3.10 This follows from $\dfrac{1}{a_{\overline{n}|i}} = \dfrac{1}{s_{\overline{n}|i}} + i$. If $j < i$ then $\dfrac{1}{s_{\overline{n}|j}} > \dfrac{1}{s_{\overline{n}|i}}$,

and $L\left[i + \dfrac{1}{s_{\overline{n}|j}}\right] = L\left[\dfrac{1}{a_{\overline{n}|i}} + \left(\dfrac{1}{s_{\overline{n}|j}} - \dfrac{1}{s_{\overline{n}|i}}\right)\right] > L\cdot\dfrac{1}{a_{\overline{n}|i}}$, which is

the outlay under amortization at rate i.

3.3.11 (a) $K\cdot s_{\overline{20}|.08} = 100,000$

$\rightarrow$ *annual payment* $= K + 12,000 = 14,185.22$

(b) *Amount in sinking fund at time loan is sold*

$= K\cdot s_{\overline{10}|.08} = 31,656.33$

(i) $14,185.22\,a_{\overline{10}|.10} = 87,162$

(ii) X where $(14,185.22 - .12X)s_{\overline{10}|.08} = X \; \rightarrow \; X = 75,042$

(c) (i) (α) $100,000 = 12,000\,a_{\overline{10}|i_\alpha} + (31,656.33 + 87,162)\cdot v_{i_\alpha}^{10}$

$i_\alpha = .130206$

(β) $\quad 14,185.22\,a_{\overline{10}|i_\beta} + 87,162\cdot v_{i_\beta}^{10} \; \rightarrow \; i_\beta = .135051$

(ii) (α) $100,000 = 12,000\,a_{\overline{10}|i_\alpha} + (31,656.33 + 75,042)v_{i_\alpha}^{10}$

$\rightarrow \; i_\alpha = .123749$

(β) $14,185.22\,a_{\overline{10}|i_\beta} + 75,042\cdot v_{i_\beta}^{10} \; \rightarrow \; i_\beta = .128183$

SECTION 3.4

3.4.1 $PV = 10,000(v^{12} + v^{24} + \cdots + v^{96})$

$$+100\left[8(v + v^2 + \cdots + v^{12}) + 7(v^{13} + \cdots + v^{24})\right.$$

$$\left. + \cdots + (v^{85} + \cdots + v^{96})\right]$$

3.4.2   (a) $K = 1000(v_{.03}^4 + v_{.03}^8 + \cdots + v_{.03}^{60}) = 1000 \cdot \dfrac{1 - v_{.03}^{60}}{(1.03)^4 - 1} = 6615.21$

$\rightarrow PV = 6615.21 + \dfrac{.04}{.03}(15,000 - 6615.21) = 17,795$

(b) $K = 1000(v^4 + 2v^8 + \cdots + 5v^{20}) = 9832.49 \rightarrow PV = 16,723$

(c) $K = 1000(5v^4 + 4v^8 + \cdots + v^{20}) = 11,504.22 \rightarrow PV = 16,165$

3.4.3   Present value of interest payments

= present value of all payments

− present value of principal payments

$$= a_{\overline{n}|j} - (v_i^n \cdot v_j + v_i^{n-1} \cdot v_j^2 + \cdots + v_i \cdot v_j^n)$$

$$= a_{\overline{n}|j} - \frac{v_i^n - v_j^n}{j - i}$$

$$= A - K = \frac{i}{j}(L - K) = \frac{i}{j}\left(a_{\overline{n}|i} - \frac{v_i^n - v_j^n}{j - i}\right)$$

3.4.4   The builder wishes a net payment of 240,000. With purchase price P, the builder receives $.10P + K + \dfrac{.005}{.0125}(.90P - K)$, where

$K = .02P(v_{.0125}^{12} + \cdots + v_{.0125}^{60}) + .80P \cdot v_{.0125}^{60} = .445025P$. Setting this equal to 240,000 results in $P = 330,117$.

3.4.5 If the rate of interest paid on outstanding balances is changed to i', then the ratio of present value of interest payments is

$$\frac{i}{i'} = \frac{A_j(i) - K_j}{A_j(i') - K_j}.$$

Also, if the interest rate on outstanding balances is equal to the valuation rate (i.e., $i = j$), then $A_j(i) = L$.

Thus, $\dfrac{A_j(i) - K_j}{L - K_j} = \dfrac{i}{j} \rightarrow A_j(i) = K_j + \dfrac{i}{j}(L - K_j)$.

3.4.6 At yield rate j per quarter, $K = 20,000 \cdot \dfrac{1 - v_j^{100}}{(1+j)^4 - 1}$, and

$$P = K + \frac{.025}{j}(500,000 - K).$$

(a) $P = 450,000 \rightarrow j = .02897 \rightarrow i^{(4)} = .1169$

(b) $P = 500,000 \rightarrow j = .025 \rightarrow i^{(4)} = .10$

(c) $P = 550,000 \rightarrow j = .02145 \rightarrow i^{(4)} = .0858$

3.4.7 The inequalities follow from the fact that $\dfrac{A - K}{L - K} = \dfrac{i}{j}$.

3.4.8 (i) At tax rate 25% the net (after-tax) rate of interest on outstanding balances is $i = .03 = j$
   $\rightarrow$ PV is (a) 15,000   (b) 15,000   (c) 15,000

(ii) At tax rate 40% the net rate of interest on outstanding balances is $i = .024$.

   (a) $PV = 6615.21 + \dfrac{.024}{.03}(15,000 - 6615.21) = 13,323$

(iii) At tax rate 60%, the net rate of interest on outstanding balances is $i = .016$.

   (a) $PV = 6615.21 + \dfrac{.016}{.03}(15,000 - 6615.21) = 11,087$

3.4.9   Merchant's Rule:
$$1000(1.10) = X[1.08+1.06+1.04+1.02+1] \rightarrow X = 211.54$$

US Rule:
$$\Big[\big[\big[[1000(1.02) - X](1.02) - X\big](1.02) - X\big](1.02) - X\Big](1.02)$$
$$- X = 0$$

$$\rightarrow \ 1000(1.02)^5 \ = \ X \cdot s_{\overline{5}|.02} \ \rightarrow \ X = 212.16$$

3.4.10   Final payment under US Rule is

$$\begin{aligned}
X \ = \ & L\big[1+t_1 i\big]\big[1+(t_2-t_1)i\big]\big[1+(t_3-t_2)i\big]\cdots\big[1+(t_n-t_{n-1})i\big] \\
& -A_1\big[1+(t_2-t_1)i\big]\big[1+(t_3-t_2)i\big]\cdots\big[1+(t_n-t_{n-1})i\big] \\
& -A_2\big[1+(t_3-t_2)i\big]\cdots\big[1+(t_n-t_{n-1})i\big] \\
& -\cdots-A_{n-1}\big[1+(t_n-t_{n-1})i\big]
\end{aligned}$$

Final payment under Merchant's Rule is

$$\begin{aligned}
Y \ = \ & L[1+t_n i]-A_1\big[1+(t_n-t_1)i\big]-A_2\big[1+(t_n-t_2)i\big] \\
& -A_{n-1}\big[1+(t_n-t_{n-1})i\big].
\end{aligned}$$

Then

$$\begin{aligned}
X-Y \ = \ & L\Big([1+t_1 i]\big[1+(t_2-t_1)i\big]\big[1+(t_3-t_2)i\big]\cdots \\
& \big[1+(t_n-t_{n-1})i\big]-[1+i_n i]\Big) \\
& -A_1\Big(\big[1+(t_2-t_1)i\big]\big[1+(t_3-t_2 i\big]\cdots\big[1+(t_n-t_{n-1})i\big]-\big[1+(t_n-t_1)i\big]\Big) \\
& -A_2\Big(\big[1+(t_3-t_2)i\big]\cdots\big[1+(t_n-t_{n-1})i\big]-\big[1+(t_n-t_2)i\big]\Big) \\
& -\cdots-A_{n-1}\Big(\big[1+(t_n-t_{n-1})i\big]-\big[1+(t_n-t_{n-1})i\big]\Big).
\end{aligned}$$

Since $L \geq A_1 + A_2 + \cdots + A_{n-1}$, it follows that $X - Y \geq$

$$A_1 \left(\left([1+t_1 i][1+(t_2-t_1)i][1+(t_3-t_2)i] \cdots [1+(t_n-t_{n-1})i] - [1+t_n i] \right) \right.$$

$$- \left([1+(t_2-t_1)i][1+(t_3-t_2)i] \cdots [1+(t_n-t_{n-1})i] - [1+(t_n-t_1)i] \right) \right)$$

$$+ A_2 \left(\left([1+t_1 i][1+(t_2-t_1)i][1+(t_3-t_2)i] \cdots \right. \right.$$

$$[1+(t_n-t_{n-1})i] - [1+t_n i] \right)$$

$$- \left([1+(t_3-t_2)i] \cdots [1+(t_n-t_{n-1})i] - [1+(t_n-t_2)i] \right) \right)$$

$$+ \cdots + A_{n-1} \left(\left([1+t_1 i][1+(t_2-t_1)i][1+(t_3-t_2)i] \cdots \right. \right.$$

$$[1+(t_n-t_{n-1})i] - [1+t_n i] \right)$$

$$- \left([1+(t_n-t_{n-1})i] - [1+(t_n-t_{n-1})i] \right) \right).$$

Since

$$\left([1+t_1 i][1+(t_2-t_1)i][1+(t_3-t_2)i] \cdots [1+(t_n-t_{n-1})i] - [1+t_n i] \right)$$

$$- \left([1+(t_2-t_1)i][1+(t_3-t_2)i] \cdots [1+(t_n-t_{n-1})i] - [1+(t_n-t_1)i] \right)$$

$$= t_1 i \left([1+t_1 i][1+(t_2-t_1)i][1+(t_3-t_2)i] \cdots \right.$$

$$[1+(t_n-t_{n-1})i] - 1 \right) \geq 0,$$

and

$$\left([1+t_1 i][1+(t_2-t_1)i][1+(t_3-t_2)i] \cdots [1+(t_n-t_{n-1})i] - [1+t_n i] \right)$$

$$- \left([1+(t_3-t_2)i] \cdots [1+(t_n-t_{n-1})i] - [1+(t_n-t_2)i] \right)$$

$$= \left[t_2 i + (t_2-t_1)i^2 \right] [1+(t_2-t_1)i][1+(t_3-t_2)i] \cdots$$

$$[1+(t_n-t_{n-1})i] - t_2 i \geq 0, \ldots,$$

it follows that $X - Y \geq 0$.

3.4.11 Bond price $1,000,000v_{.09}^{20} = 178,430.89.$

Total interest over 20 years is 821,569.11.

Straight-line method interest is $\dfrac{821,569.11}{20} = 41,078.46.$

Actuarial method interest in t^{th} year is

$178,430.89(1.09)^{t-1} \cdot (.09)$

1st year: 16,058.78; 20th year: 82,568.81

3.4.12 January 31 balance:

$$1000[1+(.15)]\frac{16}{365} = 1006.57$$

February 28 balance:

$$1006.57\left[1+(.15)\frac{28}{365}\right] = 1018.15$$

March 31 balance:

$$1018.15\left[1+(.15)\frac{31}{365}\right] + 500\left[1+(.15)\frac{30}{365}\right]$$
$$- 250\left[1+(.15)\frac{16}{365}\right] = 1285.64$$

April 30 balance:

$$1285.64\left[1+(.15)\frac{30}{365}\right] - 250\left[1+(.15)\frac{15}{365}\right] = 1049.95$$

May 31 balance:

$$1049.95\left[1+(.15)\frac{31}{365}\right]-250\left[1+(.15)\frac{16}{365}\right] = 811.69$$

June 30 balance:

$$811.69\left[1+(.15)\frac{30}{365}\right]-250\left[1+(.15)\frac{15}{365}\right] = 570.16$$

July 31 balance:

$$570.16\left[1+(.15)\frac{31}{365}\right]-250\left[1+(.15)\frac{16}{365}\right] = 325.78$$

August 15 payment required: $325.78\left[1+(.15)\frac{15}{365}\right] = 327.79$

(a) $OB_{Mar\,1} = 1000\left[1+(.15)\frac{45}{365}\right]+500 = 1518.49$

$OB_{Mar\,15} = 1518.49\left[1+(.15)\frac{15}{365}\right]-250 = 1277.85$

$OB_{Apr\,15} = 1277.85\left[1+(.15)\frac{31}{365}\right]-250 = 1044.13$

$OB_{May\,15} = 1044.13\left[1+(.15)\frac{30}{365}\right]-250 = 807.00$

$OB_{Jun\,15} = 807.00\left[1+(.15)\frac{31}{365}\right]-250 = 567.28$

$OB_{Jul\,15} = 567.28\left[1+(.15)\frac{30}{365}\right]-250 = 324.27$

Payment due August 15: $324.27\left[1+(.15)\frac{31}{365}\right] = 328.40$

(b) $1000\left[1+(.15)\frac{215}{365}\right]+500\left[1+(.15)\frac{167}{365}\right]$

$$-250\left(\left[1+(.15)\frac{153}{365}\right]+\left[1+(.15)\frac{122}{365}\right]\right.$$

$$+\left[1+(.15)\frac{92}{365}\right]+\left[1+(.15)\frac{61}{365}\right]$$

$$\left.+\left[1+(.15)\frac{31}{365}\right]\right) = 325$$

CHAPTER 4

SECTION 4.1

4.1.1 (a) $100 \cdot v_{.036}^{20} + 100(.025) \cdot a_{\overline{20}|.036} = 84.5069$

Using $P = F + F(r-j) \cdot a_{\overline{n}|j}$ it follows that $P_{(a)} < P_{(b)}$ since F is the same, $r - j$ is the same, but $j_{(a)} < j_{(b)}$. Similarly, $P_{(c)} < P_{(d)}$. Also, since $r - j = -.011 < 0$ for all of the bonds, it follows that $P_{(c)} < P_{(b)}$.

4.1.2 $115.84 = Cv_{.03}^{24} + 3.5a_{\overline{24}|.03} = .4919C + 59.27$.
Solving for C results in $C = 115$.

4.1.3 With six-month yield rate is j, $5083.49 = 10,000v_j^{20}$.
Solving for j results in $j = .0344$.
Then $X = 10,000v_j^{20} + 500a_{\overline{20}|j} = 12,229$.

4.1.4 $F \cdot v_{.025}^{16} + F(.03) \cdot a_{\overline{16}|.025} = F \cdot v_{.025}^{2n} + F(.0275) \cdot a_{\overline{2n}|.025}$
$$= F\left[v_{.025}^{2n} + 1.1(1 - v_{.025}^{2n})\right]$$
$\rightarrow \ v_{.025}^{2n} = .347250 \ \rightarrow \ 2n = 43 \ \rightarrow \ n = 21\tfrac{1}{2} \text{ years}$

4.1.5 Don invests 900 at time 0. Don's accumulated value of reinvested coupons at the end of 10 years is $40s_{\overline{20}|.03} = 1074.81$.

At the end of 10 years Don receives the redemption amount of 1000 for a total of 2074.81. If j is Don's 6-month return over the 10 year period, then $900(1 + j)^{20} = 2074.81$. Solving for j results in $j = .0426$, so that Don's nominal annual yield rate convertible semiannually over the 10 year period is .085. Note the different uses of the word "yield" in this question.

4.1.6 $800 = 1000v_j^{100} + 25a_{\overline{100}|j}$, where j is the 3-month yield rate.

Using the calculator function for unknown interest results in $j = .0316$, so the nominal annual yield rate is $4(.0316) = .1264$.

4.1.7   Bond price is $1000v_{.04}^{20} + 50a_{\overline{20}|.04} = 1135.90$, so this is the loan amount. Lump sum loan repayment amount at the end of 10 years is $1135.90(1.07)^{10} = 2234.49$.

Accumulated value of reinvested coupons at the end of 10 years is
$$50s_{\overline{20}|.03} = 1343.52.$$

Investor receives bond redemption amount of 1000 at the end of 10 years, so the net gain is
$$1343.52 + 1000 - 2234.49 = 109.03.$$

4.1.8   The bond matures exactly 5 years after issue, or 10 half-years. At a six-month yield rate of $\frac{.04855}{2} = .024275$, and coupon rate of .02375 every six months, the bond with face amount 100 would have a price of
$$100v_{.024275}^{10} + 2.375a_{\overline{10}|.024275} = 78.6746 + 20.8642 = 99.53879,$$

which rounds off to 99.539.

4.1.9   (a) The bond matures on September 1, 2009, which is exactly 5.5 years (11 half-years) after March 1, 2004 (the date for which the quote is given). The coupons are $\frac{4.25}{2} = 2.125$ every September 1 and March 1 until maturity. The 6-month yield rate is $\frac{.0369}{2} = .01845$. The bond price is
$$100v_{.01845}^{11} + 2.125a_{\overline{11}|.01845} = 102.76.$$

(b) At an annual yield rate of 3.685%, the price is 102.79 (higher price at lower yield), and at an annual yield rate of 3.695%, the price is 102.74 (lower price at higher yield).

(c) At price 102.755 the yield rate is 3.692%, and at the price of 102.765 the yield rate is 3.690%.

4.1.10 With six-month yield rate j we have

$$95.59 = 100 + 100(.02375 - j) \cdot a_{\overline{2n}|j},$$

and

$$108.82 = 100 + 100(.03125 - j) \cdot a_{\overline{2n}|j}.$$

Thus, $\dfrac{95.59 - 100}{108.82 - 100} = \dfrac{.02375 - j}{.03125 - j} \rightarrow j = .02625 \rightarrow i^{(2)} = .0525.$

4.1.11 I. $P_1 = K_1 + \dfrac{r_1}{i_1}(C - K_1) = K_1\left(1 - \dfrac{r_1}{i_1}\right) + \dfrac{r_1}{i_1} \cdot C$

and $P_2 = K_2 + \dfrac{r_2}{i_2}(C - K_2) = K_2\left(1 - \dfrac{r_2}{i_2}\right) + \dfrac{r_2}{i_2} \cdot C.$

Since $i_2 > i_1$, we have $K_2 < K_1$, so that $P_2 < P_1$. False.

II. $r_2 \cdot a_{\overline{n}|i_2} = \dfrac{r_2}{i_2}\left(1 - v_{i_2}^n\right)$ and $r_1 \cdot a_{\overline{n}|i_1} = \dfrac{r_1}{i_1}\left(1 - v_{i_1}^n\right)$ and $v_{i_2}^n < v_{i_1}^n$
$\rightarrow$ Bond 2 coupons have larger present value. True.

III. $C \cdot v_{i_2}^n < v_{i_1}^n$. False.

4.1.12 $P_1 + P_2 = 240, \ P_1 - P_2 = 24 \ \rightarrow \ P_1 = 132, P_2 = 108,$
$r_1 = 2 \cdot r_2 \qquad 132 = 100 + 100(2r_2 - .015) \cdot a_{\overline{n}|.03},$
$108 = 100 + 100(r_2 - .015) \cdot a_{\overline{n}|.03}$

$\rightarrow \ \dfrac{32}{8} = \dfrac{2r_2 - .015}{r_2 - .015} \ \rightarrow \ r_2 = .0225, \ r_1 = .045$

4.1.13 $\dfrac{79.30 - 100}{93.10 - 100} = \dfrac{.035 - j}{.045 - j} \ \rightarrow \ j = .05$

$\rightarrow \ 79.30 = 100 \cdot v_{.05}^n + 3.50 \cdot \dfrac{1 - v_{.05}^n}{.05}$

$\rightarrow \ v_{.05}^n = .31 \ \rightarrow \ n = 24$ (6-month coupon periods), or 12 years

4.1.14 $P = 1000v^{10} - (1000 - P)(.25)v^{10} + 40a_{\overline{10}|}$

$\rightarrow \ P = \dfrac{(.75)(1000)v^{10} + 40a_{\overline{10}|}}{1 - .25v^{10}} = 908.78$

4.1.15 Original purchase price: $1000v_{.05}^{40} + 40a_{\overline{40}|.05} = 828.41$

With sale price X, $828.41 = X \cdot v_{.05}^{20} + 40a_{\overline{20}|.05}$

→ $X = 875.38$.

4.1.16 $v_j^{1-t}[P_1 + Fr] = (1+j)^t \cdot v[P_1 + Fr]$.

But $v[P_1 + Fr] = P_0$.

4.1.17 Value as of October 1, 2003 was

$$100 \cdot v_{.056335}^{39} + 5.5 \cdot a_{\overline{39}|.056335} = 97.9098.$$

Value (price-plus-accrued) on February 20, 2004, which is 142 days later, is $97.9098(1.056335)^{142/182} = 102.187$.

The quoted price would be $102.187 - 5.5 \cdot \dfrac{142}{182} = 97.896$.

4.1.18 Using (4.3.E) we see that $P < C \leftrightarrow g < j$, $P = C \leftrightarrow g = j$ and $P > C \leftrightarrow g > j$.

4.1.19 $1050v^n = 210 \rightarrow v^n = .2$

→ present value of coupons

$$= 32.50 \cdot a_{\overline{n}|} = 32.50\left(\frac{1-v^n}{.04}\right) = 650$$

→ $P = 860$

4.1.20 Price of 15-year bond: $1{,}000{,}000 \cdot v_{.06}^{30} + 40{,}000 \cdot a_{\overline{30}|.06} = 724{,}703$

20-year bond price: $1{,}000{,}000 \cdot v_{.06}^{40} + 1{,}000{,}000 \cdot r \cdot a_{\overline{40}|.06} = 724{,}703$

→ $r = .041703$ (annual rate of .0834)

10-year bond price:

$1{,}000{,}000 \cdot v_{.06}^{20} + 1{,}000{,}000 \cdot r \cdot a_{\overline{20}|.06} = 724{,}703 \rightarrow r = .0354$

(annual rate of .0708)

4.1.21 i is the yield per 6-month period.

$$381.50 = Cv_i^{2n}, \quad 647.80 = Cv_i^n$$

$$\to \ v_i^n = \frac{381.50}{647.80} = .588916 \ \to \ C = 1100.$$

Price of bond X is

$$1100v^{2n} + 1000r \cdot a_{\overline{2n}|i} = 381.50 + 1000 \cdot \tfrac{r}{i} \cdot (1 - v_i^{2n})$$

$$= 381.50 + 1031.25(1 - .588916^2)$$

$$= 1055.$$

4.1.22   Let $j = \dfrac{i^{(2)}}{2}$. Then

$$v_j + r_1 \cdot v_j = v_j^2 + r_2(v_j + v_j^2)$$

$$\to \ v_j = \frac{1 + r_1 - r_2}{1 + r_2} \ \to \ j = \frac{1 + r_2}{1 + r_1 - r_2} - 1 = \frac{2r_2 - r_1}{1 + r_1 - r_2}$$

$$\to \ i^{(2)} = 2j = \frac{4r_2 - 2r_1}{1 + r_1 - r_2}$$

4.1.23 $H = \dfrac{r}{j} = \dfrac{.02}{(1.13)^{.25} - 1} = .6446$

4.1.24   Present value of coupons: $3000 \cdot \dfrac{j}{2} \cdot a_{\overline{n}|j} = 1500\left(1 - v_j^n\right)$,

Present value of redemption: $3000v^n \ \to \ v^n = \dfrac{1}{3}$

$$\to \ P = 1500\left(\frac{2}{3}\right) + 3000\left(\frac{1}{3}\right) = 2000$$

4.1.25   On November 1, 2005, present value of new bond: 1000
Present value of old bond (with bonus):

$$(1000 + X)v_{.095}^6 + 80a_{\overline{6}|.095}$$

Setting these present values equal results in $X = 114.28$.

4.1.26 $P_0(1 - t) + P_1 \cdot t = P_0(1 - t) + \left[P_0(1 + j) - Fr\right] \cdot t = P_0(1 + jt) - Frt$

4.1.27 $P_0 = (P_1 + Fr) \cdot v_j$

4.1.28 Price on August 1:

$$2000 = 1,000,000(1.05)^{44/183} - \frac{50,000}{\overline{s}_{\overline{1}|.05}} \cdot \overline{s}_{\overline{44/183}|.05} = 1,000,000$$

$$\overline{r} \cdot \overline{s}_{\overline{t}|j} = \frac{Fr}{\overline{s}_{\overline{1}|j}} \cdot \overline{s}_{\overline{t}|j} = Fr \cdot \frac{(1+j)^t - 1}{j}$$

With simple interest, $(1+j)^t$ is approximately $1 + tj$.

4.1.29 $P(n, r, j) = 100 \cdot v_j^n + 100 \cdot r \cdot a_{\overline{n}|j}$

4.1.30 (a) $g(j) = F\left[v_j^{n-t} + r(v^{1-t} + v^{2-t} + \cdots + v^{n-t})\right]$

$$\rightarrow g'(j) = \left[-F(n-t) \cdot v^{n-t+1} + r\left[(1-t) \cdot v^{2-t}\right.\right.$$

$$\left.\left. + (2-t) \cdot v^{3-t} + \cdots + (n-t) \cdot v^{n-t+1}\right]\right] \leq 0$$

and

$$g''(j) = F\left[(n-t)(n-t+1) \cdot v^{n-t+2}\right.$$

$$+ r\left[(1-t)(2-t) \cdot v^{3-t} + (2-t)(3-t) \cdot v^{4-t}\right.$$

$$\left.\left. + \cdots + (n-t)(n-t+1) \cdot v^{n-t+2}\right]\right] \geq 0$$

(b) Each term in (a) goes to $+\infty$ as $i \rightarrow -1$, since $t \leq 1$, and each term goes to 0 as $i \rightarrow \infty$.

(c) If $0 < P < \infty$, then since $g(j)$ decreases from $+\infty$ to 0 as i goes from -1 to ∞, it follows that $g(j) = P$ for exactly one value of j.

SECTION 4.2

4.2.1 Total paid: $\qquad F + n \cdot F \cdot r$

Total principal repaid: $P = F + F(r - j)a_{\overline{n}|\,j}$

Total interest paid: $\qquad n \cdot F \cdot r - F(r - j)a_{\overline{n}|\,j}$

4.2.2

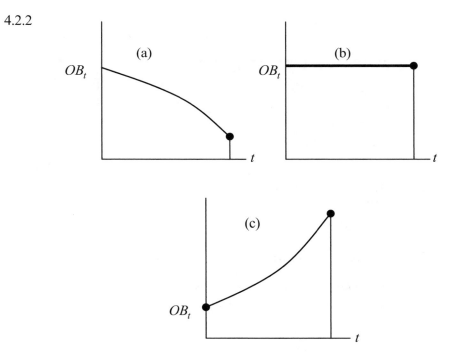

Since the adjustment in book value of outstanding balance in period $k - 1$ to k is $F(r - j) \cdot v_j^{n-k+1}$ we see that the amount is changing geometrically. If $r \geq j$ then this is principal repaid and the reduction in the outstanding balance is accelerating, so that the OB curve is concave down. The reverse is true if $r \leq j$.

4.2.3 $n = 5, \; j = .025$

t	K_t	i_t	PR_t	OB_t
1	500	279.04	220.96	10,940.49
2	500	273.51	226.49	10,714.01
3	500	267.85	232.15	10,481.86
4	500	262.05	237.95	10,243.90
5	10,500	256.10	10,243.90	0

$n = 5, \; j = .075$

t	K_t	i_t	PR_t	OB_t
1	500	674.14	– 174.14	9,162.67
2	500	687.20	– 187.20	9,349.87
3	500	701.24	– 201.24	9,551.11
4	500	716.33	– 216.33	9,767.44
5	10,500	732.56	9,767.44	0

4.2.4   As in a usual amortization,

$$OB_{t+1} = OB_t(1+j) - K_{t+1} \;\; \rightarrow \;\; 90(1.033) - 2.50 = 90.47$$

4.2.5   Amount for amortization in first coupon period:

$$F(r-j) \cdot v^n = 1.00 v_{.035}^4 = .8714$$

$$F(r-j) \cdot a_{\overline{n}|j} = 36 = (.8714)\left[1 + (1+i) + (1+i)^2 + \cdots + (1+i)^{n-1} \right]$$

$$\rightarrow \;\; s_{\overline{n}|.035} = 41.313$$

$$\rightarrow \;\; n = 26. \;\; (13 \text{ years or 26 coupon periods})$$

4.2.6   (a) $P = 10,000 \cdot v_{.04}^8 + 250 \cdot a_{\overline{8}|.04} + (.25)(P-10,000) \cdot v_{.04}^8$

$$\rightarrow \;\; P = 8764$$

4.2.7 $PR_2(1+j)^2 = PR_4 \rightarrow 977.19(1+j)^2 = 1046.79$
      $\rightarrow j = .035$ per 6 months.
      $PR_1(1+j) = PR_2 \rightarrow PR_1 = 944.14.$
      Total $PR = PR_1 + PR_2 + \cdots + PR_{30}$
$$= PR_1\left[1 + (1+j) + (1+j)^2 + \cdots + (1+j)^{29}\right]$$
$$= 944.14 s_{\overline{30}|.035} = 48,739$$

4.2.8   This follows from the fact that $P - F = F(r-j) \cdot a_{\overline{n}|j}$

4.2.9   (a) $10,000\left[(r-.04) \cdot v_{.04}\right] = -80 \rightarrow r = .03168$
          $\rightarrow P = 10,000\left[1 + (.03168-.04) \cdot a_{\overline{60}|.04}\right] = 8117.73$

      (b) $10,000\left[(r-.04) \cdot v_{.04}^{60}\right] = 80 \rightarrow r = .124157$
          $\rightarrow P = 10,000\left[1 + (.124157-.04) \cdot a_{\overline{60}|.04}\right] = 29,039.25$

      (c) $10,000\left[.04 + (r-.04)(1-v_{.04})\right] = 500 \rightarrow r = .30$
          $\rightarrow P = 68,821.07$

SECTION 4.3

4.3.1   (a)   (i)   Bond bought at discount: choose latest date of 20 years for valuation $P = 84.9537$

          (ii)   100

          (iii)   Use earliest date for valuation 117.5885

      (b)   (i)   Since the bond is bought at a discount, the minimum yield occurs if the bond is redeemed at the latest date, which is in 40 coupon periods. The 6-month yield rate j is the solution of $80 = 100 v_j^{40} + 5 a_{\overline{40}|j}$. Using a financial calculator to solve for j results in $j = .0639615$, which is quoted as an annual yield rate of $i^{(2)} = .127923$.

(ii) $i^{(2)} = .1000$

(iii) Minimum yield occurs with earliest redemption date:
$i^{(2)} = .0776$

4.3.2 (a) (i) $g = \dfrac{Fr}{C} = .0455 < j = .06$

→ Use latest redemption date: $P = 85.9259$

(ii) $g < j$ → Use latest redemption date: $P = 101.4205$

(iii) $g > j$ → Use earliest redemption date:
$P = 120.5531$

(b) (i) Purchased at a discount:
use latest redemption date for minimum yield:
$i^{(2)} = .1293$

(ii) Purchased at a discount:
use latest redemption date for minimum yield:
$i^{(2)} = .1016$

(iii) Purchased at a premium:
use earliest redemption date for minimum yield:
$i^{(2)} = .0805$

4.3.3 The bond will be bought at a discount. For a callable bond bought at a discount, the latest redemption date is the redemption date that provides the lowest price for a given yield, and the lowest yield for a given price. In order to achieve a minimum desired yield, the price that should be paid is the price paid at the latest redemption date (this is true for a callable bond bought at a discount). Therefore, the price paid is 897. If the bond is called at the end of 20 years, the annual yield rate is j, where $897 = 1050v_j^{20} + 80a_{\overline{20}|j}$. Using the calculator unknown interest function (or the BA-II PLUS bond worksheet), we get $j = .0924$.

4.3.4 g is .04 for 2016 and 2017, it is .0333 for 2018-2020, and it is .0308 for 2021-2023.

  (a) (i) Thus, $g < j = .05$ no matter when the bond is redeemed. We find the minimum price for each range of redemption dates:

  For 2016-2017 use 12/15/17: $P = 859,061$

  For 2018-2020 use 12/15/20: $P = 888,144$

  For 2021-2023 use 06/15/23: $P = 886,329$

   (ii) $j = .0325 < g$ for 2016-2020, but $j > g$ for 2021-2023.

  For 2016-2017 use earliest date 6/15/16: $P = 1,116,588$

  For 2018-2020 use earliest date 6/15/18: $P = 1,217,373$

  For 2021-2023 use latest date 6/15/23: $P = 1,252,660$

  (b) (i) Bond is bought at a discount to any redemption. We find the yield rate for the latest redemption date in each interval:

  For redemption on 12/15/17, $i^{(2)} = .1098$

  For redemption on 12/15/20, $i^{(2)} = .1126$

  For redemption on 6/15/23, $i^{(2)} = .1115$

4.3.5   Using Makeham's formula, we have $P = K + \dfrac{g}{j}(C-K)$,

  $g = .04,\ j = .05,\ C = 2,000,000$

  $K = 100,000\left[{}_{10|}\ddot{a}_{\overline{10}|.05} + 2 \cdot {}_{20|}\ddot{a}_{\overline{5}|.05} \right]$

  $= 100,000\left[\ddot{a}_{\overline{20}|} - |\ddot{a}_{\overline{10}|} + 2\left(\ddot{a}_{\overline{25}|} - \ddot{a}_{\overline{20}|} \right) \right] = 840,240$

  $\rightarrow\ P = 840,420 + \dfrac{4}{5}(2,000,000 - 840,420) = 1,768,084$

4.3.6　$P = \dfrac{100,000}{a_{\overline{20}|.05}} \cdot a_{\overline{20}|.06} = 92,037.62$

t	OB_t	K_t	I_t	PR_t
0	92,037.62			
1	89,535.61	8024.26	5522.26	2502.00
2	86,883.49	8024.26	5372.14	2652.12
3	84,072.24	8024.26	5213.01	2811.25
4	81,092.32	8024.26	5044.33	2979.92

4.3.7　　　For each t, $P_t = K_t + \frac{g}{j}(C_t - K_t)$;

then sum from $t = 1$ to $t = m$.

CHAPTER 5

SECTION 5.1

5.1.1 (a) $-(1+i)^2 + 2.3(1+i) - 1.33 = 0$

$\rightarrow$ $(2.3)^2 - 4(-1)(-1.33) = -.03 < 0$

$\rightarrow$ no real solution for $1+i$

(b) $-1 + 2.3v - 1.32v^2 = 0$

$\rightarrow$ $v = \dfrac{-2.3 \pm \sqrt{(2.3)^2 - 4(-1)(-1.32)}}{2(-1.32)} = .909091$

or .833333 $\rightarrow$ $i = .10$ or .20

5.1.2 The four transactions all have $C_0 = -1$ and $C_1 = 2.3$. Thus,

$P_i(C) = -1 + 2.3v_i + C_2 \cdot v_i^2$. Since

$C_2^a = -1.33 < C_2^b = -1.32 < C_2^c$

$= -1.3125 < C_2^d = -1.2825,$

it follows that for any positive v_i (i.e., $i > -1$),

$P_i(C_a) < P_i(C_b) < P_i(C_c) < P_i(C_d).$

5.1.3 $-5000 - 2250v_j^2 + 8137.50v_j^3 = 0 \rightarrow j = .049301$

101

5.1.4 $-5 + 3.72v_A + 4v_A^3 = 0$

$\rightarrow v_A = .797891 \rightarrow i_A = .253304$

$-5 + 3v_B + 1.7v_B^2 + 3v_B^3 = 0$

$\rightarrow v_B = .797906 \rightarrow i_B = .253280$

$P_i(C_A) > P_i(C_B) \leftrightarrow P_i(C_A) - P_i(C_B) > 0$

$\leftrightarrow .72v - 1.7v^2 + v^3 > 0$

$\leftrightarrow .72 - 1.7v + v^2 > 0$

$\leftrightarrow i < .1111$ or $i > .25$

5.1.5 (a) The IRR is the solution of the equation

$$30,000 = \frac{14,000}{1+i} + \frac{12,000}{(1+i)^2} + \frac{6,000}{(1+i)^3} + \frac{4,000}{(1+i)^4} + \frac{2,000}{(1+i)^5}.$$

The solution is $i = .1203$.

(b) The MIRR is j, which is the solution of the equation

$$30,000(1+j)^5 = 14,000(1.1)^4$$
$$+ 12,000(1.1)^3 + 6,000(1.1)^2$$
$$+ 4,000(1.1) + 2,000.$$

The solution is $j = .1081$.

(c) $NPV = -30,000 + \dfrac{14,000}{1.1} + \dfrac{12,000}{(1.1)^2} + \dfrac{6,000}{(1.1)^3}$

$+ \dfrac{4,000}{(1.1)^4} + \dfrac{2,000}{(1.1)^5} = 1,126.$

(d) $-30,000 + 14,000 = -16,000 < 0,$

$-16,000 + 12,000 = -4,000 < 0,$

$-4,000 + 6,000 = 2,000 > 0.$

The project breaks even during the third year.

(e) $-30,000 + \dfrac{14,000}{1.1} = -17,273 < 0.$

$-17,273 + \dfrac{12,000}{(1.1)^2} = -7,356 < 0,$

$-7,356 + \dfrac{6,000}{(1.1)^3} = -2,848 < 0,$

$-2,848 + \dfrac{4,000}{(1.1)^4} = -116 < 0,$

$-116 + \dfrac{2,000}{(1.1)^5} = 1,126 > 0.$

The project breaks even during the fifth year.

(f) The profitability index is

$$I = \dfrac{\dfrac{14,000}{1.1} + \dfrac{12,000}{(1.1)^2} + \dfrac{6,000}{(1.1)^3} + \dfrac{4,000}{(1.1)^4} + \dfrac{2,000}{(1.1)^5}}{30,000} = 1.0375$$

5.1.6 (a) $\dfrac{d}{di}\left[\displaystyle\sum_{s=0}^{k} C_s \cdot (1+i)^{t_k - t_s} + \sum_{s=k+1}^{n} C_s \cdot (1+i)^{t_k - t_s} \right]$

$$= \sum_{s=0}^{k} C_s \cdot (t_k - t_s) \cdot (1+i)^{t_k - t_s - 1}$$

$$+ \sum_{s=k+1}^{n} C_s \cdot (t_k - t_s) \cdot (1+i)^{t_k - t_s - 1}$$

If case (i) in the question is true, then this derivative is always negative since in the first sum the C_s's are negative and the $(t_k - t_s)$'s are positive, and in the second sum the C_s's are positive and the $(t_k - t_s)$'s are negative. The reverse is true if case (ii) is true. Thus, $\displaystyle\sum_{s=0}^{k} C_s \cdot (1+i)^{t_k - t_s} + \sum_{s=k+1}^{n} C_s \cdot (1+i)^{t_k - t_s}$ is monotonic. In case (i), as $i \to \infty$, the first part of the sum has a limit of $-\infty$ since the $(t_k - t_s)$'s are not less than 0, and the second part of the sum has a limit of 0. As $i \to -1$, the first part of the sum has a limit of 0 and the second part of the sum has a limit of $+\infty$. Since the expression is monotonic (increasing in this case) there is a unique point at which the sum is 0. The signs reverse if case (i) is true.

(d) For the function $f(j)$ in Example 5.1, the coefficients are
$C_3 = 7982.5,\ C_2 = -2295,\ C_1 = 0$ and $C_0 = -5100.$

There is exactly one sign change, so there is at most one positive root. The coefficients in the form $(-1)^n C_n$ are

$(-1)^3 C_3 = -7982.5,\qquad (-1)^2 C_2 = -2295,\qquad (-1)^1 C_1 = 0$ and
$(-1)^0 C_0 = -5100.$

Since there are no sign changes, there are no negative roots.

5.1.7 (a) Measuring time in months, we have $C_0 = -150,000,$
$C_1 = \cdots = C_5 = -1200,\ C_6 = -11,200.$
$C_7 = \cdots = C_{17} = -1200,\ C_{18} = -11,200.$
$C_{19} = \cdots = C_{23} = -1200,\ C_{24} = Y - 741,200.$
Since $C_0, \ldots, C_{23}$ are all less than 0, and $C_{24} > 0,$ condition (a) of 5.1.2 is satisfied.

(b) It is clear that $F_0, \ldots, F_{23}$ are all less than 0. In order to guarantee a unique rate of return $i > 0,$ we must have $F_{24} > 0,$
i.e., $\quad Y - 150,000 - 24(10,000) - 2(10,000) - 740,000 > 0$
$\to\ Y \geq 938,800$

5.1.8 $-150,000 - 1200 a_{\overline{24}|j} - 10,000\left(v_j^6 + v_j^{18}\right) + 260,000 v_j^{24} = 0$ (j is the monthly effective interest rate) $\to\ j = .012732$
$\to\ i^{(12)} = .1528$

5.1.9   (a) $C_0 = 1,000,000,$

$C_1 = 950,000 - (5)(10,000)\ddot{s}_{\overline{1}|.04} = 898,000,$

$C_2 = 910,000 - (4)(10,000)\ddot{s}_{\overline{2}|.04} = 825,136,$

$C_3 = 870,000 - (4)(10,000)\ddot{s}_{\overline{3}|.04} = 740,141,$

$C_4 = 840,000 - (3)(10,000)\ddot{s}_{\overline{4}|.04} = 707,510,$

$C_5 = 810,000 - (3)(10,000)\ddot{s}_{\overline{5}|.04} = 641,011,$

$C_6 = 790,000 - (2)(10,000)\ddot{s}_{\overline{6}|.04} = 652,034,$

$C_7 = 770,000 - (2)(10,000)\ddot{s}_{\overline{7}|.04} = 605,715,$

$C_8 = 750,000 - (2)(10,000)\ddot{s}_{\overline{8}|.04} = 558,344,$

$C_9 = 740,000 - (10,000)\ddot{s}_{\overline{9}|.04} = 629,939,$

$C_{10} = 730,000 - (10,000)\ddot{s}_{\overline{10}|.04} = 605,136,$

$C_{11} = 720,000 - (10,000)\ddot{s}_{\overline{11}|.04} = 579,742,$

$C_{12} = 710,000 - (10,000)\ddot{s}_{\overline{12}|.04} = 553,732,$

$C_{13} = 700,000 - (10,000)\ddot{s}_{\overline{13}|.04} = 527,081,$

$C_{14} = 690,000 - (10,000)\ddot{s}_{\overline{14}|.04} = 499,764,$

$C_{15} = -(69)(300,000) = -20,700,000$

Net profit:

$$1,000,000(1+i)^{15} + 898,000(1+i)^{14}$$
$$+ \cdots + 499,764(1+i) - 20,700,000$$

(b) $i = .0792$

5.1.10 (a) $(1+r) \cdot v^t = v \rightarrow i' = (1+r)(1+i) - 1$

(b) $10,000 \leq 1200 \left[v_{.12} + (1+r) \cdot v_{.12}^2 + \cdots + (1+r)^{14} \cdot v_{.12}^{15} \right]$

$$= 1200 \cdot \frac{1 - \left(\frac{1+r}{1.12} \right)^{15}}{.12 - r}$$

$\rightarrow r \geq .0388$

5.1.11 $-1,000,000 - 200,000 \int_0^5 e^{-\delta t} \, dt + \int_1^3 (250,000(1+t) \cdot e^{-\delta t} \, dt$

$$+ \int_3^5 (400,000)(5.5-t) \cdot e^{-\delta t} \, dt = 0$$

5.1.12 (a) Annual sinking fund deposit based on 6% rate is
$\frac{100,000}{s_{\overline{25}|.06}} = 1,822.67$. Revised deposit after 10 years is K,

where

$1,822.67 \cdot s_{\overline{10}|.06} \cdot (1.08)^{15} + K \cdot s_{\overline{15}|.08}$

$$= 100,000 \rightarrow K = 876.21.$$

Then,

$C_0 = 100,000, C_1 = \cdots = C_{10} = -11.822.67,$

$C_{11} = \cdots = C_{25} = -10,876.21 \rightarrow i = .10601$

(b) Annual payment is $\dfrac{100,000}{s_{\overline{15}|.08} + (1.08)^{15} \cdot s_{\overline{10}|.06}} = 1450.04$

$\rightarrow 100,000 = 11,450.04 a_{\overline{25}|i} \rightarrow i = .10508$

SECTION 5.2

5.2.1   Growth from 1/1/05 to 6/30/05 is

$$\frac{1,310,000 - 250,000}{1,000,000} = 1.06$$

Growth from 7/1/05 to 12/31/05 is

$$\frac{1,265,000 + 150,000}{1,310,000} = 1.080153$$

Growth from 1/1/06 to 6/30/06 is

$$\frac{1,540,000 - 250,000}{1,265,000} = 1.019763$$

Growth from 7/1/06 to 12/31/06 is

$$\frac{1,420,000 + 150,000}{1,540,000} = 1.019481$$

Annual time-weighted return for 2005-2006 is

$$\sqrt{(1.06)(1.080153)(1.019763)(1.019481)} - 1 = .0910.$$

5.2.2   Time-weighted: $\frac{12}{10} \cdot \frac{X}{12 + X} = 1 \;\rightarrow\; X = 60.$

Dollar-weighted: $10(1+i) + 60\left(1 + \tfrac{1}{2}i\right) = 60 \;\rightarrow\; i = -.25.$

5.2.3   At dollar-weighted rate x in 2005 the fund value at the end of the year is

$$100,000(1+x) - 8000\left(1+\tfrac{3}{4}x\right).$$

At time weighted rate x in 2006 the accumulated fund value at the end of 2006 is

$$\left[100,000(1+x) - 8000\left(1+\tfrac{3}{4}x\right)\right](1+x),$$

which we are told is equal to 103,992. Therefore,

$$\left[100,000(1+x) - 8000\left(1+\tfrac{3}{4}x\right)\right](1+x) = 103,992.$$

We can expand the equation and get a quadratic equation in x, obtaining $x = .0625$ (we ignore the negative root).

5.2.4   The 6-month time-weighted return is $\left(\tfrac{40}{50}\right)\left(\tfrac{80}{60}\right)\left(\tfrac{157.50}{160}\right) = 1.05$

→   annual effective rate of interest is .1025.

One-year time-weighted yield is $\left(\tfrac{40}{50}\right)\left(\tfrac{80}{60}\right)\left(\tfrac{175}{160}\right)\left(\tfrac{X}{250}\right) = 1.1025$

→ $X = 236.25$.

5.2.5   Time-weighted: Return for first half-year is −20%, return for second half-year is 25%. Time-weighted return is $(1-.20)(1+.25) - 1 = 0$.

Dollar-weighted: 100,000 units purchased January 1, 2005 and 125,000 units purchased July 1, 2005. Value on January 1, 2006 is 225,000. Money-weighted return is i where

$$100,000(1+i) + 100,000\left(1+\tfrac{1}{2}i\right)$$
$$= 225,000 \quad \to \quad i = .1667.$$

5.2.6   K: $100(1+i) - X\left(1+\frac{1}{2}i\right) + 2X\left(1+\frac{1}{4}i\right) = 125$

$\rightarrow X = 125 - 100(1+i),$

L: $\dfrac{125}{100} \cdot \dfrac{105.8}{125 - X} = 1+i \rightarrow X = 125 - \dfrac{132.25}{1+i}$

$\rightarrow 125 - 100(1+i) = 125 - \dfrac{132.25}{1+i}$

$\rightarrow 100(1+i) = \dfrac{132.25}{1+i} \rightarrow (1+i)^2 = 1.3225 \rightarrow i = .15.$

SECTION 5.3

5.3.1   (a) $\dfrac{2I}{F(0) + F(1) - I} = \dfrac{120}{500 + 620 - 60} = .1132$

(b) (i) $\dfrac{120}{600 + 620 - 60} = .1034$

(ii) $F(t) = 500 + 20t$ for $0 \le t \le \dfrac{1}{4}$, and

$F(t) = 600 + 20t$ for $\dfrac{1}{4} \le t \le 1$

$\rightarrow \displaystyle\int_0^1 F(t)\, dt = \int_0^{1/4} F(t)\, dt + \int_{1/4}^1 F(t)\, dt$

$= 125.625 + 459.375 = 585$

$\rightarrow i \doteq \dfrac{120}{2(585) - 60} = .1081$

(iii) $\displaystyle\int_0^1 F(t)\, dt = 560 \rightarrow i \doteq \dfrac{120}{2(560) - 60} = .1132$

(iv) $\displaystyle\int_0^1 F(t)\, dt = 535 \rightarrow i \doteq \dfrac{120}{2(535) - 60} = .1188$

(v) $\displaystyle\int_0^1 F(t)\, dt = 510 \rightarrow i \doteq \dfrac{120}{2(510) - 60} = .125$

5.3.2 $\quad i = \dfrac{I}{F(t_1) + \frac{N}{2}} = \dfrac{2I}{2F(t_1) + N}.$ But

$$F(t_2) = F(t_1) + N - I$$

$$\rightarrow \quad N = F(t_2) - F(t_1) + I$$

$$\rightarrow \quad i = \dfrac{2I}{F(t_1) + F(t_2) - I}.$$

5.3.3 Suppose that t is the point at which the balance in the account first becomes positive. Then

$$16{,}147 = -10{,}000(1.15)^t \cdot (1.09)^{10-t}$$
$$+ X \cdot s_{\overline{t}|.15} \cdot (1.09)^{10-t} + X \cdot s_{\overline{10-t}|.09}$$

From Example 5.6 we see from Investment 1 that $X \le 3000$ so that $t \ge 5$.

Try $t = 5: \rightarrow X = 2878.85.$ But then balance at time 5 is

$$-10{,}000(1.15)^5 + 2878.85 \cdot s_{\overline{5}|.15} = -703.28,$$

which is contrary to our assumption that $t = 5$.

Try $t = 6: \rightarrow X = 2882.37.$ Then the balance at $t = 6$ is
$-10{,}000(1.15)^6 + 2878.85 \cdot s_{\overline{6}|.15} = 2100.88,$ and the balance at $t = 5$ is $-10{,}000(1.15)^5 + 2878.85 \cdot s_{\overline{5}|.15} = -703.27.$

Thus, $t = 6$ is the first point at which the balance is positive, $X = 2882.37.$

CHAPTER 6

6.1.1 $P = \dfrac{10}{1.15} + \dfrac{10}{(1.1)^2} + \dfrac{110}{(1.05)^3} = 111.98$

$111.98 = 100v_j^3 + 10a_{\overline{3}|j} \rightarrow j = .0556.$

6.1.2 $P = \dfrac{100}{(1.12)^4} + (5)\left[\dfrac{1}{(1.1)} + \dfrac{1}{(1.1)^2} + \dfrac{1}{(1.12)^3} + \dfrac{1}{(1.12)^4}\right] = 78.97.$

6.1.3 (a) The present value of 1 due in t years at the annual t-year spot rate $s_0(t)$ convertible semiannually is $\left(1 + \frac{1}{2} \cdot s_0(t)\right)^{-2t}$. Since each $s_0(t)$ is nominal convertible semiannually, the total present value of all coupons and redemption amount is

(i) $5\left[(1.0375)^{-1} + (1.03875)^{-2} + (1.04)^{-3} + (1.04)^{-4}\right.$

$\left. + (1.04125)^{-5} + (1.0425)^{-6}\right]$

$+ 100(1.0425)^{-6} = 104.05.$

(ii) $5\left[(1.07)^{-1} + (1.06875)^{-2} + (1.0675)^{-3} + (1.06625)^{-4}\right.$

$\left. + (1.065)^{-5} + (1.06375)^{-6}\right]$

$+ 100(1.06375)^{-6} = 93.15.$

(iii) $5 \cdot a_{\overline{6}|.06} + 100(1.06)^{-6} = 95.08.$

(b) We find nominal annual yield rates of (i) 8.44%, (ii) 12.82%, and (iii) 12%. It is obvious that the yield rate in (iii) must be 12%, since the price is based on a constant spot rate of 12%.

6.1.4 (a) $85.12 = 100(1+s_0(20))^{-20} + 2\sum_{k=1}^{20}(1+s_0(k))^{-k}$

$133.34 = 100(1+s_0(20))^{-20} + 5\sum_{k=1}^{20}(1+s_0(k))^{-k}$

$s_0(k)$ is the 6-month yield on a zero-coupon bond maturing in k 6-month periods.

$48.22 = 133.34 - 85.12$

$= 3\sum_{k=1}^{20}(1+s_0(k))^{-k} \rightarrow \sum_{k=1}^{20}(1+s_0(k))^{-k} = 16.07$

$100(1+s_0(20))^{-20} = 52.97 \rightarrow s_0(20) = .0323$; this is the 6-month yield rate for a zero-coupon bond maturing in 20 6-month periods. The annual yield (as a rate convertible semi-annually) is .0646.

(b) The bond price can be represented using the term structure:

$$P = (1+s_0(n))^{-n} + r\sum_{k=1}^{n}(1+s_0(k))^{-k}.$$

The bond price can also be represented using the YTM j:

$$P = (1+j)^{-n} + r\sum_{k=1}^{n}(1+j)^{-k}.$$

If $j < s_0(1) = s_0(2) = \cdots = s_0(n-1) < s_0(n)$,

then $(1+j)^{-k} > (1+s_0(k))^{-k}$ for $k = 1, 2, \ldots, n$ so that

$$(1+j)^{-n} + r\sum_{k=1}^{n}(1+j)^{-k} > (1+s_0(n))^{-n} + r\sum_{k=1}^{n}(1+s_0(k))^{-k},$$

which contradicts the pricing consistency.

If $j > s_0(n) > s_0(1) = s_0(2) = \cdots = s_0(n-1)$,

then $(1+j)^{-k} < (1+s_0(k))^{-k}$ for $k = 1, 2, \ldots, n$ so that

$$(1+j)^{-n} + r\sum_{k=1}^{n}(1+j)^{-k} < (1+s_0(n))^{-n} + r\sum_{k=1}^{n}(1+s_0(k))^{-k},$$

which again contradicts the pricing consistency. Therefore, it must be the case that

$$s_0(1) = s_0(2) = \cdots = s_0(n-1) < j < s_0(n).$$

6.1.5 ½-year zero coupon rate: ½-year YTM = .05(.025 per ½-year).

1-year bond:
$$P = \frac{.03}{1.05} + \frac{1.03}{(1.05)^2} = .962812 = \frac{.03}{1.025} + \frac{1.03}{(1+j)^2}$$

→ $j = .0504$ → 1-year zero coupon rate = .10078.

1½-year bond: $P = \dfrac{.02}{1.075} + \dfrac{.02}{(1.075)^2} + \dfrac{1.02}{(1.075)^3}$

$$= .856971 = \frac{.02}{1.025} + \frac{.02}{(1.0504)^2} + \frac{1.02}{(1+j)^3}$$

→ $j = .075755$ → 1½-year zero coupon rate = .15151.

2-year bond:

$$P = \frac{.04}{1.075} + \frac{.04}{(1.075)^2} + \frac{.04}{(1.075)^3} + \frac{1.04}{(1.075)^4}$$

$$= .882774 = \frac{.04}{1.025} + \frac{.04}{(1.0504)^2} + \frac{.04}{(1.07576)^3} + \frac{1.04}{(1+j)^4}$$

→ $j = .07617$ → 2-year zero coupon rate = .15234.

6.1.6   (a) $H(r,t)$ is the YTM for a bond maturing at time t with coupon
rate r. Suppose that the bond has a face amount 1. The price of
the bond can be expressed in terms of YTM or term structure
and the two prices are the same.

YTM Price:

$$[1+H(r,t)]^{-t} +r\left([1+H(r,t)]^{-1} +[1+H(r,t)]^{-2}\right.$$

$$\left. +\cdots+[1+H(r,t)]^{-t}\right),$$

Term Structure Price:

$$[1+H(0,t)]^{-t} +r\left([1+H(0,1)]^{-1} +[1+H(0,2)]^{-2}\right.$$

$$\left. +\cdots+[1+H(0,t)]^{-t}\right).$$

Suppose that $H(0,t)$ is a decreasing function of t for all t, so
that $H(0,1) > H(0,2) > \cdots > H(0,t)$.

Suppose also that $H(r,t) < H(0,t)$.

Therefore, $H(0,1) > H(0,2) > \cdots > H(0,t) > H(r,t)$ and it
follows that

$$[1+H(r,t)]^{-1} > [1+H(0,1)]^{-1},$$

$$[1+H(r,t)]^{-2} > [1+H(0,2)]^{-2},\ldots, \text{ and }$$

$$[1+H(r,t)]^{-t} > [1+H(0,t)]^{-t}.$$

This contradicts the assumption that the YTM price is the
same as the term structure price. It therefore follows that
$H(r,t) < H(0,t)$ must be false, so that $H(r,t) \geq H(0,t)$
must be true.

Suppose that $r_1 \geq r_2$. The YTM's $H(r_1,t)$ and $H(r_2,t)$ satisfy the relationships

(i) YTM Price (coupon rate r_1):

$$[1+H(r_1,t)]^{-t} + r_1\left([1+H(r_1,t)]^{-1} + [1+H(r_1,t)]^{-2}\right.$$
$$\left. + \cdots + [1+H(r_1,t)]^{-t}\right)$$

Term Structure Price (coupon rate r_1):

$$[1+H(0,t)]^{-t} + r_1\left([1+H(0,1)]^{-1} + [1+H(0,2)]^{-2}\right.$$
$$\left. + \cdots + [1+H(0,t)]^{-t}\right)$$

and

(ii) YTM Price (coupon rate r_2):

$$[1+H(r_2,t)]^{-t} + r_2\left([1+H(r_2,t)]^{-1} + [1+H(r_2,t)]^{-2}\right.$$
$$\left. + \cdots + [1+H(r_2,t)]^{-t}\right)$$

Term Structure Price (coupon rate r_2):

$$[1+H(0,t)]^{-t} + r_2\left([1+H(0,1)]^{-1} + [1+H(0,2)]^{-2}\right.$$
$$\left. + \cdots + [1+H(0,t)]^{-t}\right)$$

It follows that

$$[1+H(r_1,t)]^{-t} - [1+H(r_2,t)]^{-t}$$
$$+ r_1\sum_{k=1}^{t}[1+H(r_1,t)]^{-k} - r_2\sum_{k=1}^{t}[1+H(r_2,t)]^{-k}$$
$$= (r_1-r_2)\sum_{k=1}^{t}[1+H(0,k)]^{-k}.$$

If $H(r_1,t) < H(r_2,t)$, then

(iii) $\left[1+H(r_1,t)\right]^{-t}-\left[1+H(r_2,t)\right]^{-t}$

$$+r_1\sum_{k=1}^{t}\left[1+H(r_1,t)\right]^{-k}-r_2\sum_{k=1}^{t}\left[1+H(r_2,t)\right]^{-k}$$

$$> \left[1+H(r_2,t)\right]^{-t}-\left[1+H(r_2,t)\right]^{-t}+(r_1-r_2)\sum_{k=1}^{t}\left[1+H(r_2,t)\right]^{-k}$$

$$= (r_1-r_2)\sum_{k=1}^{t}\left[1+H(r_2,t)\right]^{-k}.$$

From comments above, we know that $H(r_2,t)\geq H(0,t)$, and it then follows from (ii) above that

$$\sum_{k=1}^{t}\left[1+H(r_2,t)\right]^{-k}>\sum_{k=1}^{t}\left[1+H(0,k)\right]^{-k}.$$

Putting these relationships together, we see that if

$$H(r_1,t) < H(r_2,t),$$

then

$$(r_1-r_2)\sum_{k=1}^{t}\left[1+H(0,k)\right]^{-k}$$

$$= \left[1+H(r_1,t)\right]^{-t}-\left[1+H(r_2,t)\right]^{-t}+r_1\sum_{k=1}^{t}\left[1+H(r_1,t)\right]^{-k}$$

$$-r_2\sum_{k=1}^{t}\left[1+H(r_2,t)\right]^{-k} > (r_1-r_2)\sum_{k=1}^{t}\left[1+H(r_2,t)\right]^{-k}$$

$$> (r_1-r_2)\sum_{k=1}^{t}\left[1+H(0,k)\right]^{-k},$$

which is impossible. It follows that the assumption $H(r_1,t) < H(r_2,t)$ must be false, showing that

$$H(r_1,t) \geq H(r_2,t) \geq H(0,t).$$

(b) and (c) Similar to (a), but reverse the inequalities.

SECTION 6.3

6.3.1 (a) $(1+s_0(k-1))^{k-1} \cdot (1+i_0(k-1,k)) = (1+s_0(k))^k$

$$\rightarrow \quad i_0(k-1,k) = \frac{(1+s_0(k))^k}{(1+s_0(k-1))^{k-1}} - 1$$

(b) $1+i_0(1,2) = \dfrac{(1+s_0(2))^2}{1+s_0(1)}$

$$\rightarrow \quad (1+s_0(1))(1+i_0(1,2)) = (1+s_0(2))^2$$

We proceed by induction:

If $(1+i_0(0,1))(1+i_0(1,2)) \cdots (1+i_0(k-2,k-1)) = (1+s_0(k-1))^{k-1}$,

then since $1+i_0(k-1,k) = \dfrac{(1+s_0(k))^k}{(1+s_0(k-1))^{k-1}}$,

it follows that

$$(1+s_0(1))(1+i_0(1,2)) \cdots (1+i_0(k-2,k-1))(1+i_0(k-1,k))$$
$$= (1+s_0(k-1))^{k-1}(1+i_0(k-1,k)) = (1+s_0(k))^k.$$

(c) From part (a), $\dfrac{d}{ds_0(k)}i_0(k-1,k) = \dfrac{k(1+s_0(k))^{k-1}}{(1+s_0(k-1))^{k-1}} > 0$, and

$$\frac{d}{ds_0(k-1)}i_0(k-1.k) = \frac{-(k-1)(1+s_0(k))^k}{(1+s_0(k-1))^k} < 0.$$

(d) If $s_0(k) > s_0(k-1)$, then

$$i_0(k-1,k) = \frac{(1+s_0(k))^k}{(1+s_0(k-1))^{k-1}} - 1$$

$$= (1+s_0(k))\left(\frac{1+s_0(k)}{1+s_0(k-1)}\right)^{k-1} - 1 > 1+s_0(k) - 1$$

$$= s_0(k).$$

6.3.2 (a) Using the formulations in Exercise 6.3.1 for

$$i_0(k-1,k) = \frac{(1+s_0(k))^k}{(1+s_0(k-1))^{k-1}} - 1,$$

we have in case (i),

$$i_0(1,2) = \frac{(1+s_0(2))^2}{1+s_0(1)} - 1 = \frac{(1.092)^2}{1.091} - 1 = .0930.$$

The table of values of $i_0(k-1,k)$ is

k	(i)	(ii)
1	.0910	.0919
2	.0930	.0953
3	.0950	.0981
4	.0970	.1003
5	.0990	.1019
6	.1010	.1029
7	.1030	.1033
8	.1050	.1031
9	.1070	.1023
10	.1090	.1009

6.3.3 The 6-month rate of interest for a 6-month maturity T-Bill is

$$j_0 = \frac{100}{97.800} - 1 = .02249.$$

The 1-year effective rate of interest for 1-year maturity T-Bill is

$$i = \frac{100}{95.4} - 1 = .04822.$$

The 6-month forward, 6-month interest rate is j, where

$$(1.02249)(1+j) = 1.04822 \quad \rightarrow \quad j = .02516,$$

which is quoted as a nominal annual rate of .0503 compounded semiannually.

6.3.4 1-year forward effective annual rate of interest is:

$$\frac{(1.1)^2}{1.08} - 1 = .1204,$$

2-year forward effective annual rate of interest:

$$\frac{(1.11)^3}{(1.1)^2} - 1 = .1303.$$

6.3.5 (a) (i) $\quad i_0(1,2) = \dfrac{(1.07)^2}{1.06} - 1 = .0801$ (.08 close enough)

(ii) $\quad i_0(2,3) = \dfrac{(1.09)^3}{(1.07)^2} - 1 = .1311.$

(b) $\quad i_0(3,4) = \dfrac{(1+s_0(4))^4}{(1+s_0(3))^3} - 1 = \dfrac{(1+s_0(4))^4}{(1+.09)^3} - 1 \geq i_0(2,3) = .1311.$

$\rightarrow \quad (1+s_0(4))^4 \geq (1.09)^3(1.1311) \quad \rightarrow \quad s_0(4) \geq .1001$

6.3.6 $\quad 73.68 = 100(1+s_0(5))^{-5}$

$$+5\left[\frac{1}{(1.1)} + \frac{1}{(1.1)^2} + \frac{1}{(1.12)^3} + \frac{1}{(1.12)^4} + (1+s_0(5))^{-5} \right]$$

$$= 105(1+s_0(5))^{-5} + 15.41$$

$\rightarrow \quad s_0(5) = .125 \quad \rightarrow \quad i_0(4,5)$

$$= \frac{(1+s_0(5))^5}{(1+s_0(4))^4} - 1$$

$$= \frac{(1.125)^5}{(1.12)^4} - 1 = .1452.$$

6.3.7 (a) (i) $i_0(t-1,t) = \dfrac{(1+s_0(t))^t}{(1+s_0(t-1))^{t-1}} - 1$. Since $i_{0,t}$

increases with t, it follows that $\dfrac{1+s_0(t)}{1+s_0(t-1)} \geq 1$, so that

$$i_0(t-1,t) = \frac{(1+s_0(t))^{t-1} \cdot (1+s_0(t))}{(1+s_0(t-1))^{t-1}} - 1 \geq s_0(t).$$

(ii) Reverse the inequalities in (i).

(b) (i) This is illustrated in Exercise 6.3.2 for yield curve (ii) in years 7 to 10.

(ii) This can be done by constructing a quadratic yield curve with positive second derivative.

6.3.8 $r_t = \dfrac{1}{t}\int_0^t \delta_s \, ds \rightarrow$

(i) and (ii) $\displaystyle\lim_{t\to\infty} r_t = \lim_{t\to\infty} \frac{\int_0^t \delta_s \, ds}{t} = \lim_{t\to\infty} \delta_t$ (l'Hospital's rule).

SECTION 6.4

6.4.1 Receive $\dfrac{1000}{1.1} = 909.09$ from sale of one-year zero. Invest for two

years and receive $909.09(1.08)^2 = 1,060.36$ at the end of two years.

Pay back 1000 at the end of 1 year. Net result is a 1-year forward investment for one year. Amount invested in one year is 1000, and amount received a year after that is 1060.36; 1-year forward rate of interest is .0604.

6.4.2 Borrow low (7% in year from now), invest high (forward rate of $\frac{(1.07)^2}{1.06} - 1 \geq .0801$ one year from now). At time 0 sell a 1-year zero coupon bond with maturity amount 1. Receive $\frac{1}{1.06} = .9434$. Also at time 0, with the .9434 buy a 2-year zero coupon bond with maturity amount $(.9434)(1.07)^2 = 1.0801$ at time 2.

At time 1, borrow 1 for one year at 7% (agreeing to pay 1.07 at time 2), and pay the maturity amount on the 1-year zero sold at time 0. At time 2, receive 1.0801 and pay the accumulated loan amount of 1.07. Net gain is $1.0801 - 1.07 = .0101$ with net investment of 0.

6.4.3 Receive $\frac{1000}{(1.1)^2} = 826.45$ from sale of 2-year zero. Invest for one year and receive $826.45(1.08) = 892.56$ at the end of one year.

Pay back 1000 at the end of 2 years. Net result is a 1-year forward loan for one year. Loan amount received in one year is 892.56, paid back a year after that is 1000; 1-year forward rate of interest is $\frac{1000}{892.56} - 1 = .12$.

6.4.4 (a) For 100 bond,

$$P = 105(1+.005x)^{-3} + 5\left[(1.04)^{-1} + (1.05)^{-2}\right]$$

$$= 100(1.055)^{-3} + 5\left[(1.055)^{-1} + (1.055)^{-2} + (1.055)^{-3}\right]$$

$$= 98.65 \;\rightarrow\; x = 11.09$$

(b) $(1.05)^2(1.055) = (1+.005x)^3 \;\rightarrow\; x = 10.33$.

(c) Sell a 6-month zero (say face amount 100) and receive $100(1.04)^{-1} = 96.15$, and buy a 1-year zero with maturity value $96.15(1.05)^2 = 106.01$. In 6 months, borrow 100. If your prediction is correct, you will owe $100(1.05) = 105$ at the end of the year. Your 1-year zero matures for 106.01 and you pay 105, with a profit of 1.01.

6.4.5 Net proceeds at the end of the 2nd year are

$$(1.085)^2 - (1.08)(1+i) > 0 \quad \rightarrow \quad i < \frac{(1.085)^2}{1.08} - 1 = .09002.$$

6.4.6 The swap rate is j in the solution of

$$j \times \left[\frac{1}{1+s_0(1)} + \frac{1}{(1+s_0(2))^2} + \cdots + \frac{1}{(1+s_0(n))^n} \right]$$

$$= \frac{i_0(0,1)}{1+s_0(1)} + \frac{i_0(1,2)}{(1+s_0(2))^2} + \cdots + \frac{i_0(n-1,n)}{(1+s_0(n))^n}.$$

With the given term structure, the forward rates are

$$i_0(0,1) = .05, \quad i_0(1,2) = \frac{(1.1)^2}{1.05} - 1 = .152381,$$

$$i_0(2,3) = \frac{(1.15)^3}{(1.1)^2} - 1 = .256921,$$

$$i_0(3,4) = \frac{(1.2)^4}{(1.15)^3} - 1 = .363426.$$

Solving for j results in $j = .1774$.

Note that this is the same as the at-par yield for the term structure in Example 6.8.

6.4.7 (a) and (b)

$$1 + i_0(t-1,t) = \frac{(1+s_0(t))^t}{(1+s_0(t-1))^{t-1}},$$

so that

$$\frac{1 + i_0(t-1,t)}{1 + s_0(t)} = \frac{(1+s_0(t))^{t-1}}{(1+s_0(t-1))^{t-1}}.$$

Assume that $i_0(t-1,t) > s_0(t)$. Then

$$\frac{(1+s_0(t))^{t-1}}{(1+s_0(t-1))^{t-1}} = \frac{1 + i_0(t-1,t)}{1 + s_0(t)} > 1 \ \Rightarrow\ s_0(t) > s_0(t-1),$$

and therefore $s_0(t)$ is an increasing function of t for all t.
A similar argument applies if $i_0(t-1,t) < s_0(t)$ for all t.

Assume that $s_0(t)$ is an increasing function of t for all t, so that $s_0(1) < s_0(2) < \cdots < s_0(t-1) < s_0(t)$. Then

$$i_0(t-1,t) = \frac{(1+s_0(t))^t}{(1+s_0(t-1))^{t-1}} - 1$$

$$= \frac{(1+s_0(t))^{t-1}}{(1+s_0(t-1))^{t-1}} \cdot (1 + s_0(t)) - 1.$$

Since $s_0(t) > s_0(t-1)$ it follows that $\dfrac{(1+s_0(t))^{t-1}}{(1+s_0(t-1))^{t-1}} > 1$ and then

$$i_0(t-1,t) > 1 + s_0(t) - 1 = s_0(t).$$

A similar argument applies if $s_0(t)$ is a decreasing function of t for all t.

(c) and (d)

It is always true that $i_0(0,1) = s_0(1)$.

Suppose that $i_0(t-1,t)$ is an increasing function of t for all t, so that $i_0(0,1) < i_0(1,2) < \cdots$. Then $s_0(t) < i_0(t-1,t)$ for $t \geq 2$.

This is true since

$$(1+s_0(t))^t = (1+i_0(0,1))(1+i_0(1,2)) \cdots (1+i_0(t-1,t))$$
$$< (1+i_0(t-1,t))^t,$$

so that $1+s_0(t) < 1+i_0(t-1,t)$. Then

$$(1+s_0(2))^2 = (1+i_0(0,1))(1+i_0(1,2)) > (1+i_0(0,1))^2 = (1+s_0(1))^2,$$

and it follows that $s_0(2) > s_0(1)$. Then

$$(1+s_0(t))^t = (1+s_0(t-1))^{t-1}(1+i_0(t-1,t))$$
$$> (1+s_0(t-1))^{t-1}(1+i_0(t-2,t-1)) \geq (1+s_0(t-1))^t,$$

so that $s_0(t) > s_0(t-1)$, i.e., s_t is an increasing function of t.

Suppose that s_t is an increasing function of t for all t, so that $s_0(1) < s_0(2) < \cdots$. For a t-period coupon bond with coupon and at-par yield r_t we have $(1+s_0(t))^{-t} + r_t \cdot \sum_{k=0}^{t}(1+s_0(k))^{-k} = 1$.

It follows that $r_t < s_t$, for if $r_t \geq s_0(t)$, then

$$r_t \geq s_0(t) > s_0(t-1) > \cdots > s_0(2) > s_0(1), \text{ so that}$$

$$1 = (1+r_t)^{-t} + r_t \cdot \sum_{k=0}^{t}(1+r_t)^{-k} < (1+s_0(t))^{-t} + r_t \cdot \sum_{k=0}^{t}(1+s_0(k))^{-k},$$

which contradicts the definition of at-par yield which has

$$(1+s_0(t))^{-t} + r_t \cdot \sum_{k=0}^{t}(1+s_0(k))^{-k} = 1.$$

Therefore, $r_t < s_0(t)$.

For a $(t-1)$-period coupon bond with coupon and at-par yield r_{t-1} we have $(1+s_0(t-1))^{-(t-1)} + r_{t-1} \cdot \sum_{k=0}^{t-1} (1+s_0(k))^{-k} = 1$.

For the t-period coupon bond with coupon and at-par yield r_t we have $(1+s_0(t))^{-t} + r_t \cdot \sum_{k=0}^{t} (1+s_0(k))^{-k} = 1$. We can rewrite this in the form $(1+s_0(t))^{-t}(1+r_t) + r_t \cdot \sum_{k=0}^{t-1} (1+s_0(k))^{-k} = 1$.

Since $r_t < s_0(t)$ it follows that

$$1 = (1+s_0(t))^{-t}(1+r_t) + r_t \cdot \sum_{k=0}^{t-1} (1+s_0(k))^{-k}$$

$$< (1+s_0(t))^{-(t-1)} + r_t \cdot \sum_{k=0}^{t-1} (1+s_0(k))^{-k}.$$

But then

$$(1+s_0(t-1))^{-(t-1)} + r_{t-1} \cdot \sum_{k=0}^{t-1} (1+s_0(k))^{-k}$$

$$= 1 < (1+s_0(t))^{-(t-1)} + r_t \cdot \sum_{k=0}^{t-1} (1+s_0(k))^{-k}$$

from which it follows that $r_{t-1} < r_t$.

Similar arguments apply if $i_0(t-1,t)$ is a decreasing function of t for all t.

CHAPTER 7

SECTION 7.1

7.1.1 Macauley duration:

$$\frac{(3)(100)\left(\frac{1}{1.118}\right)^3 + (10)\left[\frac{1}{1.118} + 2\left(\frac{1}{1.118}\right)^2 + 3\left(\frac{1}{1.118}\right)^3\right]}{(100)\left(\frac{1}{1.118}\right)^3 + (10)\left[\frac{1}{1.118} + \left(\frac{1}{1.118}\right)^2 + \left(\frac{1}{1.118}\right)^3\right]}$$

$$= \frac{261.1}{95.7} = 2.73$$

7.1.2 $D = \dfrac{\sum\limits_{t=1}^{n} t \cdot F \cdot r \cdot v_j^t + n \cdot F \cdot v_j^n}{\sum\limits_{t=1}^{n} F \cdot r \cdot v_j^t + F \cdot v_j^n}$. If $r = j$, then the denominator is

$$F \cdot j \cdot a_{\overline{n}|j} + F \cdot v_j^n = F \rightarrow D = j \cdot (Ia)_{\overline{n}|j} + n \cdot v_j^n = \ddot{a}_{\overline{n}|j}.$$

If $r = j = .10$, and $n = 6$ then $D = 4.7908$.

7.1.3 Using the formulation in Example 7.3, for $j = .03$ we have the following values:

| | \multicolumn{4}{c}{n} |
r	2	10	20	40
.04	1.96189	8.50869	14.5725	22.4642
.06	1.94491	8.06690	13.5336	20.8770
.08	1.92911	7.73080	12.8493	19.9706

With n and j held fixed, D is a decreasing function of r.
With r and j held fixed, D is an increasing function of n.
With r and n held fixed, D is an decreasing function of j.

7.1.4 $\quad P = (1+j)^{-n} + ra_{\overline{n}|j} = (1+j)^{-n} + r\left[\dfrac{1-(1+j)^{-n}}{j}\right]$

$\rightarrow \quad \dfrac{dP}{dj} = -n(1+j)^{-n-1} + r\left[\dfrac{jn(1+j)^{-n-1} - \left[1-(1+j)^{-n}\right]}{j^2}\right]$

$D = -(1+j)\dfrac{dP/dj}{P}$

$= \dfrac{n(1+j)^{-n} - r(1+j)\left[\dfrac{jn(1+j)^{-n-1} - \left[1-(1+j)^{-n}\right]}{j^2}\right]}{(1+j)^{-n} + r\left[\dfrac{1-(1+j)^{-n}}{j}\right]} \cdot \dfrac{(1+j)^n}{(1+j)^n}$

$= \dfrac{n - r(1+j)\left[\dfrac{jn(1+j)^{-1} - [(1+j)^n - 1]}{j^2}\right]}{1 + r\left[\dfrac{(1+j)^n - 1}{j}\right]}$

$= \dfrac{nj - r(1+j)\left[\dfrac{jn(1+j)^{-1} - \left[(1+j)^n - 1\right]}{j}\right]}{j + r\left[(1+j)^n - 1\right]}$

$= \dfrac{nj - nr + r\left(\dfrac{1+j}{j}\right)\left[(1+j)^n - 1\right]}{j + r\left[(1+j)^n - 1\right]}$

$= \dfrac{nj - nr + r\left(\dfrac{1+j}{j}\right)\left[(1+j)^n - 1\right] + \left(\dfrac{1+j}{j}\right)j - (1+j)}{j + r\left[(1+j)^n - 1\right]}$

$= \dfrac{1+j}{j} - \dfrac{1 + j + n(r-j)}{j + r\left[(1+j)^n - 1\right]}$

This is the duration based on 6-month periods (since j is the 6-month YTM). It is divided by 2 to get the Macaulay duration based on an annual period.

7.1.5 An annuity is like a bond with coupons of 1 per period and maturity value of 0.

$$D = \frac{(Ia)_{\overline{n}|}}{a_{\overline{n}|}} = \frac{\ddot{a}_{\overline{n}|} - nv^n}{1 - v^n}$$

$$= \frac{\ddot{a}_{\overline{n}|}}{1 - v^n} - \frac{nv^n}{1 - v^n} = \frac{1}{d} - \frac{n}{(1+i)^n - 1}$$

$$= \frac{1}{d} - \frac{n}{is_{\overline{n}|}}$$

7.1.6 The Macaulay duration of the portfolio is
$$\frac{F_1 \times .8835 \times 12.7 + F_2 \times 1.3049 \times 14.6}{F_1 \times .8835 + F_2 \times 1.3049} = 13.5.$$

Since $F_1 + F_2 = 100$, we solve the two equations to get

$$F_1 = 67.01 \text{ and } F_2 = 32.99.$$

The portfolio value is

$$67.01(.8835) + 32.99(1.3049) = 102.25.$$

7.1.7 (a) $1 + \frac{1}{j}$

(b) 1 (if $n=1$)

(c) $\dfrac{(Ia)_{\overline{n}|j}}{a_{\overline{n}|j}}$

(d) n

(e) 1

(f) $\dfrac{\frac{n(n+1)\cdot r}{2} + n}{n \cdot r + 1}$

7.1.8 $\quad \dfrac{d}{di}\left[L(1+i)^D\right] \;=\; (1+i)^D \cdot \dfrac{dL}{di} + L \cdot D(1+i)^{D-1}$

But $\dfrac{dL}{di} \;=\; -\dfrac{D \cdot L}{1+i} \;\rightarrow\; \dfrac{d}{di}\left[L(1+i)^D\right] \;=\; 0$

7.1.9 $\quad$ (a) $\; L \;=\; r\cdot \overline{a}_{\overline{n}|j} + v_j^n \;=\; r\displaystyle\int_0^n e^{-\delta t}\,dt + e^{-\delta n}$

$\rightarrow\; \dfrac{dL}{d\delta} \;=\; -r(\overline{I}\,\overline{a})_{\overline{n}|} - n\cdot e^{-\delta n}$

7.1.10 $\quad D \;=\; \dfrac{nv^n + r(Ia)_{\overline{n}|}}{v^n + ra_{\overline{n}|}} \;\rightarrow\; \dfrac{dD}{dr} \;=\; \dfrac{(v^n + ra_{\overline{n}|})(Ia)_{\overline{n}|} - \left(nv^n + r(Ia)_{\overline{n}|}\right)a_{\overline{n}|}}{(v^n + ra_{\overline{n}|})^2}$

$$= \dfrac{v^n (Ia)_{\overline{n}|} - nv^n a_{\overline{n}|}}{(v^n + ra_{\overline{n}|})^2}$$

$$= \dfrac{v^n}{(v^n + ra_{\overline{n}|})^2} \cdot \left[(Ia)_{\overline{n}|} - na_{\overline{n}|}\right].$$

$(Ia)_{\overline{n}|} - na_{\overline{n}|} \;=\; \displaystyle\sum_{t=1}^{n} tv^t - n\sum_{t=1}^{n} v^t$

$$= \displaystyle\sum_{t=1}^{n} (t-n)v^t \;\leq\; 0 \;\rightarrow\; \dfrac{dD}{dr} \leq 0$$

7.1.11 $\dfrac{d}{d\alpha}\displaystyle\sum_{t=1}^{6} K_t\left[1+\tfrac{1}{2}(s_0(.5t)+\alpha)\right]^{-t}$

$$= -\frac{1}{2}\sum_{t=1}^{6} tK_t\left[1+\tfrac{1}{2}(s_0(.5t)+\alpha)\right]^{-t-1}.$$

At $\alpha=0$ this is

$$-\tfrac{1}{2}\Big(5\big[(1.0375)^{-2}+2(1.03875)^{-3}$$

$$+\cdots+6(1.0425)^{-7}\big]-600(1.0425)^{-7}\Big)$$

$$= -\tfrac{1}{2}[84.86+448.35] = -267.$$

$$\dfrac{d}{d\alpha}\sum_{t=1}^{6} K_t\left[1+\tfrac{1}{2}(.0990+\alpha)\right]^{-t} = -\frac{1}{2}\sum_{t=1}^{6} tK_t\left[1+\tfrac{1}{2}(.0990+\alpha)\right]^{-t-1}.$$

At $\alpha=0$ this is

$$-\tfrac{1}{2}\Big(5(1.0495)^{-1}(Ia)_{\overline{6}|.0495}+600(1.0495)^{-7}\Big)$$

$$= -\tfrac{1}{2}[67.12+427.83] = -247.$$

7.1.12 Current duration is $\dfrac{(50,000)(8)+(30,000)(6)}{50,000+30,000} = 7.25.$

To reduce duration, sell x of the 8-year duration bond and buy 6-year duration bond. $\dfrac{(50,000-x)(8)+(30,000+x)(6)}{50,000+30,000} = 7$

→ $x=10,000.$ Answer (e)

7.1.13 $D = \dfrac{nv^n+r(Ia)_{\overline{n}|}}{v^n+ra_{\overline{n}|}}$

→ $\dfrac{dD}{dr} = \dfrac{\left(v^n+ra_{\overline{n}|}\right)(Ia)_{\overline{n}|}-(nv^n+r(Ia)_{\overline{n}|})a_{\overline{n}|}}{(v^n+ra_{\overline{n}|})^2}$

$$= \dfrac{v^n\left[(Ia)_{\overline{n}|}-na_{\overline{n}|}\right]}{(v^n+ra_{\overline{n}|})^2} < 0. \qquad \text{Answer (b)}$$

7.1.14 $\quad D = \sum t \cdot w_t = \sum t \cdot \dfrac{K_t v^t}{L} \quad \rightarrow \quad \dfrac{d}{dj} D$

$$= \sum t \dfrac{d}{dj} w_t = \sum t \cdot \dfrac{d}{dj}\left(\dfrac{K_t v^t}{L}\right)$$

$$\dfrac{d}{dj} w_t = \dfrac{d}{dj}\left(\dfrac{K_t v^t}{L}\right) = \dfrac{-LtK_t v^{t+1} + K_t v^{t+1} LD}{L^2}$$

$$= \dfrac{LK_t v^{t+1}(D-t)}{L^2}$$

Since $K_t > 0$ for at least two values of t, $1 < D < n$, and there must be an integer t_0 such that $1 < t_0 < n$ and $t_0 \le D \le t_0 + 1$. Then, for $t = 1, 2 + \cdots + t_0$, $\dfrac{d}{dj} w_t > 0$ and for $t = t_0 + 1, \ldots, n$, $\dfrac{d}{dj} w_t < 0$. Then

$$\dfrac{d}{dj} D = \sum t \dfrac{d}{dj} w_t = \sum_{t=1}^{t_0} t \cdot \dfrac{d}{dj} w_t + \sum_{t=t_0+1}^{n} t \cdot \dfrac{d}{dj} w_t$$

$$\le t_0 \cdot \sum_{t=1}^{t_0} \dfrac{d}{dj} w_t + (t_0 + 1) \cdot \sum_{t=t_0+1}^{n} \dfrac{d}{dj} w_t.$$

For any j, $\sum w_t = 1$, so that

$$\dfrac{d}{dj} \sum w_t = \sum \dfrac{d}{dj} w_t = 0 \quad \rightarrow \quad \sum_{t=t_0+1}^{n} \dfrac{d}{dj} w_t = -\sum_{t=1}^{t_0} \dfrac{d}{dj} w_t,$$

and then

$$\dfrac{d}{dj} D \le t_0 \cdot \sum_{t=1}^{t_0} \dfrac{d}{dj} w_t + (t_0 + 1)\left(-\sum_{t=1}^{t_0} \dfrac{d}{dj} w_t\right) = -\sum_{t=1}^{t_0} \dfrac{d}{dj} w_t < 0.$$

7.1.15 $D = \dfrac{\sum\limits_{t=1}^{n} t K_t (1+j)^{-t}}{\sum\limits_{t=1}^{n} K_t (1+j)^{-t}}$

$= \dfrac{K_1(1+j)^{-1} + 2K_2(1+j)^{-2} + \cdots + nK_n(1+j)^{-n}}{K_1(1+j)^{-1} + K_2(1+j)^{-2} + \cdots + K_n(1+j)^{-n}}$

$= \dfrac{K_1 + 2K_2((1+j)^{-1} + \cdots + nK_n(1+j)^{-n+1}}{K_1 + K_2(1+j)^{-1} + \cdots + K_n(1+j)^{-n+1}}$

$\lim\limits_{j \to \infty} = \dfrac{K_1}{K_1} = 1.$

SECTION 7.2

7.2.1 (a) Purchasing x_1 units of bond 1 and x_2 units of bond 2, we have cash flow of $1.01x_1 + .02x_2$ at time 1 and $1.02x_2$ at time 2. Thus, $x_2 = \dfrac{1}{1.02} = .980392$ and $1.01x_1 + .02x_2 = 1$

$\rightarrow x_1 = .970685$.

Cost $= (.970685)\left(\dfrac{1.01}{1.14}\right) + (.980392)\left(\dfrac{.02}{1.15} + \dfrac{1.02}{1.15^2}\right)$

$= 1.633187$.

(b) Purchasing x_1 units of bond 1 and x_2 units of bond 3, we have cash flow of $1.01x_1 + .2x_2$ at time 1 and $1.2x_2$ at time 2. Thus,

$x_2 = \dfrac{1}{1.2} = .833333$ and $1.01x_1 + .2x_2 = 1 \rightarrow x_1 = .825083$.

Cost $= (.825083)\left(\dfrac{1.01}{1.14}\right) + (.833333)\left(\dfrac{.2}{1.1495} + \dfrac{1.2}{1.1495^2}\right)$

$= 1.632786$.

(c) Combination (a) and (b) are the only possibilities for exact matching.

7.2.2 $pv_L(.10) = 300,000;$

$n = 5, \ X \cdot a_{\overline{5}|.10} = 300,000 \ \rightarrow \ X = 79,139;$

$n = 15, \ X = 39,442; \ n = 50, \ X = 30,257; \ n = 100, \ X = 30,002$

n	$\sum tA_t v^t$	$\sum t^2 A_t v^t$
5	843,048	2,962,020
15	1,833,680	16,896,161
50	3,171,124	60,020,920
100	3,297,823	69,034,390

From Example 7.7, $\sum tL_t v^t = 2,262,077$. The nearest match occurs at $n = 15$. Exact match occurs at $n = 20$, but there is no immunization in that case.

7.2.3   (a) $\dfrac{d}{di} PV_A(i)\Big|_{i_0} = -\sum tA_t v_{i_0}^{t+1}$, and similarly for L

(b) $\dfrac{d^2}{di^2} PV_A(i)\Big|_{i_0} = \sum t(t+1) A_t v_{i_0}^{t+2}$

Since $PV_A(i_0) = PV_L(i_0)$, so that $\sum A_t v_{i_0}^t = \sum L_t v_{i_0}^t$ and $\dfrac{d}{di} PV_A(i)\Big|_{i_0} = \dfrac{d}{di} PV_L(i)\Big|_{i_0}$, so that $\sum tA_t v_{i_0}^t = \sum tL_t v_{i_0}^t$,

it follows that

$$\sum \left[-2tD(i_0) + D(i_0)^2 \right] A_t v_{i_0}^t = \sum \left[-2tD(i_0) + D(i_0)^2 \right] L_t v_{i_0}^t.$$

Also, $\dfrac{d^2}{di^2} PV_A(i)\Big|_{i_0} > \dfrac{d^2}{di^2} PV_L(i)\Big|_{i_0}$ is equivalent to

$\sum t(t+1) A_t v_{i_0}^{t+2} > \sum t(t+1) L_t v_{i_0}^{t+2}$, which, in turn, is equivalent

to $\sum t^2 A_t v_{i_0}^t > \sum t^2 L_t v_{i_0}^t$ since $\sum tA_t v_{i_0}^t = \sum tL_t v_{i_0}^t$.

The result then follows from the fact that

$$\left(t - D(i_0)\right)^2 = t^2 - 2tD(i_0) + D(i_0)^2.$$

7.2.4 For the liability of 30,000 at $t = 1$, we have

$$A_0 + A_{15} \cdot v_{.10}^{15} = 30,000 v_{.10} = 27,272.73, \text{ and}$$

$$15 \cdot A_{15} \cdot v_{.10}^{15} = 30,000 v_{.10}$$

$$\rightarrow A_{15} = 7595.00, \quad A_0 = 25,454.55$$

7.2.5 (a) $A_5 v^5 + A_{15} v^{15} = v^{10} = .385543,$

$$5 A_5 v^5 + 15 A_{15} v^{15} = 10 v^{10} = 3.855433$$

$$\rightarrow A_{15} = .805255, \quad A_5 = .310461$$

(b) (i) $.4 v^5 + A_{t_2} v^{t_2} = .385543, \quad 2 v^5 + t_2 A_{t_2} v^{t_2} = 3.855433$

$$\rightarrow t_2 = 19.053, \quad A_{t_2} = .8432$$

(ii) $.7 v^5 + A_{t_2} v^{t_2} = .385543, \quad 3.5 v^5 + t_2 A_{t_2} v^{t_2} = 3.855433$

$$\rightarrow A_{t_2}, \; t_2 < 0$$

(c) (i) $t_2 = 21.28, \quad A_5 = .4302$ or $t_2 = 11,27, \quad A_5 = .1258$
(ii) $t_2 = 31.92, \quad A_5 = .5056$
(iii) no solution

(d) (i) $t_1 = 9.21, \quad A_{t_2} = .2213$
(ii) no solution with $t_1 \leq 10$
(iii) no solution

(e) $t_1 = 4.74, \quad t_2 = 20.223$

7.2.6 $A_{t_0} v_{.10}^{t_0} + 15,000 \ddot{a}_{\overline{12}|.10} = 1,000,000 v_{.10}^{12}$

$$t_0 \cdot A_{t_0} v_{.10}^{t_0} + 15,000 (Ia)_{\overline{11}|.10} = 12 \cdot 1,000,000 v_{.10}^{12}$$

$$\rightarrow t_0 = 16.15, \quad A_{t_0} = 961,145$$

7.2.7 (a) $\dfrac{A_1}{1.1}+\dfrac{A_5}{(1.1)^5} = 100\left(\dfrac{1}{(1.1)^2}+\dfrac{1}{(1.1)^4}+\dfrac{1}{(1.1)^6}\right)$,

$\rightarrow\quad \dfrac{A_1}{1.1}+\dfrac{A_5}{(1.1)^5} = 207.39,$

Note that there was an implied multiplication of 1.1.

$\dfrac{A_1}{1.1}+\dfrac{5A_5}{(1.1)^5} = 100\left(\dfrac{2}{(1.1)^2}+\dfrac{4}{(1.1)^4}+\dfrac{6}{(1.1)^6}\right)$

$\rightarrow\quad \dfrac{A_1}{1.1}+\dfrac{5A_5}{(1.1)^5} = 777.18,$

Solving for A_1 and A_5 results in $A_5 = 229.41,\quad A_1 = 71.44.$

(b) $\dfrac{2A_1}{1.1}+\dfrac{6\cdot5A_5}{(1.1)^5} = 4403,\ 100\left(\dfrac{2\cdot1}{(1.1)^2}+\dfrac{5\cdot4}{(1.1)^4}+\dfrac{6\cdot5}{(1.1)^6}\right) = 3225$

Since $4403 > 3225$, Redington immunization is satisfied at 10%.

7.2.8 (a) $h(i) = 149,194.85 + 629,950.53 v_i^{15}$

$\qquad -\left[10,000(a_{\overline{10}|i}+a_{\overline{12}|i}+a_{\overline{15}|i})+100,000(v_i^{10}+v_i^{12}+v_i^{15})\right]$

$h'(i) = 10,000v_i\left[(Ia)_{\overline{10}|i}+(Ia)_{\overline{12}|i}+(Ia)_{\overline{15}|i}\right]$

$\qquad +100,000\left(10v_i^{11}+12v_i^{13}\right)-7,949,258v_i^{16}$

Regarding $h'(i)$ as a polynomial in v_i we see that there is only one sign change in the coefficients of the increasing powers of v_i. It follows from the rule of signs that there is only one positive solution of v_i to the relationship $h'(i) = 0$. Noting that $h'(.10) = 0$, it follows that this is the unique solution.

Noting that $h(0) = 109,135 > 0$, and $\lim\limits_{i\to\infty} h(i) = 149,195 > 0$, and $h(.10) = 0$, we see that $h(i)$ has its overall minimum at $i = .10$. In order for $h(i)$ to have a minimum at a point other than $i = .10$ there would have to be another point for which $h'(i) = 0$.

(b) At

$$i = 1000\%, \quad h(i) = 195,407.21 v_i^2 + 525,977.96 v_i^{14}$$
$$- \left[10,000(a_{\overline{10}|i} + a_{\overline{12}|i} + a_{\overline{15}|i}) + 100,000(v_i^{10} + v_i^{12} + v_i^{15}) \right]$$
$$\rightarrow \quad h(1000) = -29.8$$

7.2.9   (a) $(s-t_1) A_{t_1} v_{i_0}^{t_1} = (t_2-s) A_{t_2} v_{i_0}^{t_2}$

      (b) $L_s = A_{t_1} \cdot v^{t_1-s} \left(1 + \dfrac{s-t_1}{t_2-s} \right)$

7.2.10   (a) $h(.03) = 40,851, \quad h(.08) = 2,170,$
             $h(.12) = 1,595, \quad\;\; h(.20) = 23,154$

       (b) $h(.03) = -12,596, \quad h(.08) = -690,$
             $h(.12) = -514, \quad\;\;\; h(.20) = -7,524$

       (c) $h(.03) = 18,968, \quad h(.08) = 994,$
             $h(.12) = 714, \quad\;\;\;\;\; h(.20) = 9,738$

7.2.11   (a)   Two linear equations in unknowns A_{t_1} and A_{t_2}. There is a unique solution of $t_1 \neq t_2$.

       (b)   Solve for t_1 from $t_1 = \dfrac{sL_s v^s - t_2 A_{t_2} v^{t_2}}{L_s v^s - A_{t_2} v^{t_2}}$, then solve for A_{t_1}.

          The condition guarantees that the denominator exceeds 0.

       (c)   Similar to (b).

       (d)   From Exercise 7.2.9(b) we can reduce to an equation in t_1 alone and use an approximation method to solve for t_1.

7.2.12 (i) Let $X = $ cash now and $Y = $ maturity amount of 10-year zero.

$$X + Yv_{.08}^{10} \; = \; X + .463193Y \; = \; 6710.1$$

$$10Yv_{.08}^{10} = 4.63193Y = 32{,}686.9 \; \rightarrow \; Y = 7057, \; X = 3441.$$

(ii) Let $x = $ additional cash needed now.

Then $x + Cv_{.08}^{10} = 5000v_{.08}^{11}$ and

$$10Cv_{.08}^{10} = 11(5000)v_{.08}^{11} \; \rightarrow \; C = 5092.59, \; x = -214.44.$$

Then $100(7057+5093)v_{.08}^{10} \; = \; 562{,}780$ which is greater than

$$\sum_{k=1}^{11} L_k \cdot k^2 v^k \; = \; \sum_{k=1}^{10} L_k \cdot k^2 v^k + L_{11}(121)v^{11}$$
$$= \; 212{,}969 + 259{,}474 \; = \; 472{,}443.$$

Therefore, at $j = .08$ the assets immunize the liabilities. Answer: (c)

7.2.13 (a) $PV_1 \; = \; A(1+j)^{-5} + B(1+j)^{-10} + C(1+j)^{-15}$
$\qquad\qquad = \; X(1+j)^{-6} + Y(1+j)^{-12} \; = \; PV_2$ - Equation 1

In one period,

$PV_1' \; = \; A(1+j)^{-4} + B(1+j)^{-9} + C(1+j)^{-14}$
$\qquad = \; PV_1(1+j) \; = \; PV_2(1+j)$
$\qquad = \; X(1+j)^{-5} + Y(1+j)^{-11} \; = \; PV_2'$

(b) If PV's are equal, then

$$D_1 = \frac{-(1+j)\frac{d}{dj}PV_1}{PV_1} = \frac{-(1+j)\frac{d}{dj}PV_2}{PV_2} = D_2$$

$$\Leftrightarrow -(1+j)\frac{d}{dj}PV_1 = -(1+j)\frac{d}{dj}PV_2.$$

Thus,

$$-(1+j)\frac{d}{dj}PV_1 = 5A(1+j)^{-5} + 10B(1+j)^{-10} + 15C(1+j)^{-15}$$

$$= -(1+j)\frac{d}{dj}PV_2 = 6X(1+j)^{-6} + 12Y(1+j)^{-12}$$

– Equation 2.

Subtracting Equation 1 from Equation 2 we get

$$4A(1+j)^{-5} + 9B(1+j)^{-10} + 14C(1+j)^{-15}$$
$$= 5X(1+j)^{-6} + 11Y(1+j)^{-12},$$

and then multiplying by $(1+j)$ we get

$$4A(1+j)^{-4} + 9B(1+j)^{-9} + 14C(1+j)^{-14}$$
$$= 5X(1+j)^{-5} + 11Y(1+j)^{-11},$$

so that $\frac{d}{dj}PV_1' = \frac{d}{dj}PV_2'$ one period from now. PV's are equal and derivatives of PV's are equal one period from now, the Macaulay durations are equal one period from now.

(c) $D_1' = \dfrac{4A(1+j)^{-4} + 9B(1+j)^{-9} + 14C(1+j)^{-14}}{A(1+j)^{-4} + B(1+j)^{-9} + C(1+j)^{-14}}$ is the Macauley

duration of the first set of cashflows one period from now. We then have

$$D_1' = \frac{4A(1+j)^{-4} + 9B(1+j)^{-9} + 14C(1+j)^{-14}}{A(1+j)^{-4} + B(1+j)^{-9} + C(1+j)^{-14}}$$

$$= \frac{4A(1+j)^{-5} + 9B(1+j)^{-10} + 14C(1+j)^{-15}}{A(1+j)^{-5} + B(1+j)^{-10} + C(1+j)^{-15}}$$

(multiply numerator and denominator by $(1+j)^{-1}$), and then

$$\frac{5A(1+j)^{-5} + 10B(1+j)^{-10} + 15C(1+j)^{-15} - \left[A(1+j)^{-5} + B(1+j)^{-10} + C(1+j)^{-15}\right]}{A(1+j)^{-5} + B(1+j)^{-10} + C(1+j)^{-15}}$$

$$= D_1 - 1.$$

CHAPTER 8

8.1.1   (a) $PV = 50 \cdot v_{.15}^{10} + \sum_{t=1}^{10} (1.05)^{t-1} \cdot v_{.15}^{t}$

$$= 12.3592 + \frac{1 - \left(\frac{1.05}{1.15}\right)^{10}}{.15 - .05} = 18.3329$$

(b) $20.00 = X \cdot v_{.15}^{10} + \sum_{t=1}^{10} (1.05)^{t-1} \cdot v_{.15}^{t} = 2472X + 12.3592$

$\rightarrow \quad X = 56.74$

8.1.2 $25 = \dfrac{2}{.12 - r} \rightarrow r = .04$

The equivalent dividend at the end of the first year is

$$.50 s_{\overline{4}|.03} = 2.0918.$$

Thus the present value of all dividends is

$$25 = \frac{2.0918}{i - s},$$

where

$$i = (1.03)^4 - 1 = .125509$$

is the equivalent annual effective rate of interest, so that $s = .0418$.

SECTIONS 8.2 AND 8.3

8.2.1   (a)   Net gain = Gain on short sale – dividends payable =

$$(500)(120{-}100) - (500)(4) \; = \; 8000.$$

           (b)   Amount invested: $(500)(120)(.5) \; = \; 30,000.$
Balance in margin account after short position is closed on August 31 is

$$30,000(1.01)^3 - (500)(4)(1.01)$$
$$+ (500)(120{-}100) \; = \; 38,889.03$$

      3-month rate of return is

$$\frac{38,889.03 - 30,000}{30,000} \; = \; .2963 \,(29.63\%)$$

8.2.2   Smith's gain is:

Interest on margin account plus return on short sale minus commission paid.

The margin required: $(.50)(1000)(10) = 5000$

Interest on margin account: $(.05)(5000) = 250$

Return on short sale: $(1000)(10{-}X) = 10,000 - 1000X$

Commission paid: $(1000)(10)(.01) + 1000X(.01) \; = \; 100 + 10X$

Total gain: $250 + 10,000 - 10,000X - (100{+}10X)$
$$= \; 10,150 - 1010X \; = 100$$
$$\to \;\; X = 9.95$$

8.2.3   Bill's account: $500(1.06) + 1000 - P - X \; = \; 500(1.21)$
Jane's account: $500(1.06) + 1000 - (P{-}25) - 2X \; = \; 500(1.21).$
Solving two equations in P and X results in $P = 900.$

8.2.4   Chris's return: $\dfrac{P-760+.5P(.06)}{.5P} = \dfrac{1.03P-760}{.5P}$

Jose's return: $\dfrac{P-760+.5P(.06)-32}{.5P} = \dfrac{1.03P-792}{.5P}$

$$\dfrac{1.03P-760}{.5P} = 2\cdot\dfrac{1.03P-792}{.5P} \;\rightarrow\; P=800$$

$\rightarrow$ Chris's return: .16

SECTION 8.4

8.4.1   (a) $75,000,000\Big[(.90)(v_{.09}+v^2+v^3+v^4)$

$+(.80)(v^5+v^6+v^7+v^8)+(.75)(v^9+v^{10})\Big]$

$+1,000,000,000(.75)\cdot v^{10} \;=\; 722,854,822$

(b) $i^{(2)}=.250$

(c) $P = 722,854,822+1,000,000,000(.15)\cdot v^{10}$

$= 786,216,443$

$i^{(2)} = .223$

CHAPTER 9

9.1.1 (a) $K = S_0 e^{rT} = 2000 e^{.05} = 2102.54.$

(b) The no arbitrage price is \$2102.54 (from part (a)). A riskless profit can be obtained in the following way:

(i) Take a short position on a one year forward contract with forward (delivery) price 2150 where the other party is willing to take the long position.

(ii) Borrow 2000 at the risk-free rate for one year and buy one ounce of platinum.

(iii) At the end of the year, deliver the platinum and receive 2000; the loan is paid back with amount

$$2000 e^{.05} = 2102.54.$$

and a riskless profit of

$$2150 - 2102.54 = 47.46$$

is made.

(c) The value of the long position of the contract is

$$f_t = S_t - Ke^{-r(T-t)},$$

so that

$$f_{.50} = 2000 - 2102.54 e^{-.05(.50)} = -50.63.$$

9.1.2   (a) (i)   1-year forward price is $900e^{.08} = 974.96$

          (ii) 2-year forward price is $900e^{2(.08)} = 1056.16$.

   (b) Value of the 2-year long forward contract is

$$S_1 - 900e^{2(.08)}e^{-.08}.$$

Value of the 3-year short contract is

$$900e^{3(.08)}e^{-2(.08)} - S_1.$$

Combined value is 0.

   (c) Value of the 2-year long forward contract is

$$S_1 - 900e^{2(.08)}e^{-.10}.$$

Value of the 3-year short contract is

$$900e^{3(.08)}e^{-2(.10)} - S_1.$$

Combined value is

$$900e^{3(.08)}e^{-2(.10)} - 900e^{2(.08)}e^{-.10} = -18.92.$$

9.1.3   (a) The spot price at the time the contract is entered is the spot price of a 31-year bond:

$$S_0 = 100e^{-31(.06)} + 4\left(\frac{1-e^{-31(.06)}}{e^{.06/2}-1}\right) = 126.46.$$

The no arbitrage one year forward price is

$$(S_0-I)e^r = (126.46-4e^{-.03}-4e^{-.06})e^{.06} = 126.15.$$

   (b) Since the forward price is below the no arbitrage forward price, arrange to buy in one year at the lower price. The strategy is as follows:

      (i)   Take a long position in a one year forward contract on the bond.

      (ii)   Sell short a 31 year 8% T-Bond, receive 126.46.

(iii)   Invest 126.46 for one year at risk free rate.

(iv)   At $t = .5$, borrow 4 for 6 months at risk free rate, and pay coupon to person to which the bond was sold.

(v)   At $t = 1$, receive $126.46e^{.06} = 134.28$ from 1 year investment; pay coupon of 4 and 6-month loan amount of $4e^{.03} = 4.12$, and close forward contract by buying 30- year T-Bond for 125 and delivering to the party to whom it was sold short one year ago; this leaves a riskless profit of $134.28 - 4 - 4.12 - 125 = 1.16$. The riskless profit is the difference between the no arbitrage forward price and the actual forward price as of time 0.

(c) The spot price when the contract is entered is

$$S_0 = 100v_{.03}^{62} + 4\left(\frac{1 - v_{.03}^{62}}{.03}\right) = 128.00.$$

The no arbitrage one year forward price is
$$(128.00 - 4e^{-.025} - 4e^{-.05})e^{.05} = 126.46.$$

This is the delivery price of a 30-year 8% bond. The yield to maturity as a 6-month rate is the solution to the equation.

$$126.46 = 100v_j^{60} + 4\left(\frac{1 - v_j^{60}}{j}\right) \rightarrow j = .03036 \rightarrow \text{annual}$$

yield to maturity compounded semiannually is .0607.

9.1.4   The margin required is 1200. The next day, the value of the account has dropped by $(5000)(4.95 - 4.90) = 250$ to 950, which is below the maintenance margin. The additional margin required is 250. The one day percentage loss is $\frac{250}{1200} = 20.83\%$.

9.1.5   Note that the convention for quoting the price of a futures contract on a 3-month banker's acceptance is as follows. A price of 92.00 for the contract means that when the futures contract expires, the 1-year nominal rate of discount convertible every 3-months on the bankers acceptance that is to be delivered is 8.00% (8.00 = 100.00-92.00). The 3-month return on the 3-month banker's acceptance will be 2.00%, so the 3-month banker's acceptance that is delivered is a 3-month investment in which $98 is invested and $100 is returned 3 months later (the rate of 2% is a 3-month discount rate).

(a) The 1,000,000 is received in January, and when the futures contract is sold in January, there is a loss on the futures contract: $(93.60 - 94.00) \times 2500 = -1000$.

The net amount invested in January at 1.625% (1/4 of 6.5%) is 999,000, which grows to 1,015,233.75 in April. This is a net return of 1.523% for 3 months, or 6.09% annualized (nominal convertible quarterly).

(b) The 1,000,000 is received in January, and when the futures contract is sold in January, there is a gain on the futures contract of $(94.40 - 94.00) \times 2500 = 1000$.

The net amount invested in January at 1.375% (1/4 of 5.5%) is 1,001,000, which grows to 1,014,763.75 in April. This is a net return of 1.476% for 3 months, or 5.90% annualized (nominal convertible quarterly).

(c) The 1,000,000 is received in January, and when the futures contract is sold in January, there is a gain on the futures contract of $(100 - k - 94.00) \times 2500 = 15,000 - 2500k$.

The net amount invested in January at $\frac{i}{400}$ (1/4 of i%) is $1,000,000 + 15,000 - 2500k$, which grows to

$$(1,015,000 - 2500k) \times (1 + \tfrac{i}{4})$$

in April. This is a net return of

$$\left[\frac{(1,015,000 - 2500k) \times (1 \times \tfrac{i}{4})}{1,000,000} - 1 \right] \times 4$$

annualized (compounded quarterly).

9.1.6 The 1,000,000 is received in January, and when the futures contract is sold in January, there is a loss on the futures contract of 2500 (this is $96.00 - 95.00 = 1.00 = 100 \times (.01)$).

The net amount invested in January at 1.25% (1/4 of 5%) is 997,500, which grows to 1,009,968.75 in April. This is a net return of .996875% for 3 months (or 3.98% annualized, nominal convertible quarterly).

9.1.7 Each .01 increase in futures contract price results in $25 loss on the short contract. Loss for the week is $250, which is −50% of $500.

9.1.8 The delivery price for a one year forward contract on the bond, with delivery immediately after the coupon payment:

$$K = \left(860 - 40e^{-.08(.50)} - 40e^{-.10(1)}\right)e^{.10(1)}$$

$$= \left[860e^{.08(.50)} - 40\right]e^{.12(.50)} - 40 = 867.97$$

9.1.9 (a) $K = (S_0 - I)(1.05)^2 = \left[76.00 - \dfrac{4}{1.05} - \dfrac{4}{(1.05)^2}\right](1.05)^2 = 75.59.$

(b) $f_{.50} = (F_{.50} - K)(1.05)^{-1}$

$F_{.50} = (S_{.50} - I_{.50})(1.05) = \left[76.50 - \dfrac{4}{1.05}\right](1.05) = 76.325$

$\rightarrow f_{.50} = (76.325 - 75.59)(1.05)^{-1} = .70.$

9.1.10 Delivery price on original contract is $K = S_0 e^{2r}$. Forward contract price in one year is $G - Ke^{-\delta} = G - S_0 e^{2r-\delta}$.

9.1.11 Futures price is $1000e^{(.08-.03)(.25)} = 1012.58.$

9.1.12 The implied 3-month forward 3-month rate of interest is

$$\frac{1+(.06)\left(\frac{1}{2}\right)}{1+(.057)\left(\frac{1}{4}\right)} - 1 = .0155$$

3-month Banker's Acceptance pv is $\frac{100}{1.0155} = .9847.$

Quoted as $1-4(1-.9847) = .9388$, according to the convention described in the solution to 9.1.5.

9.1.13 In order for there to be no arbitrage opportunity, we must have

$$(P-3e^{-r/2} - 3e^{-r})e^{r} = Pe^{r} - 3e^{r/2} - 3 = 92.00.$$

i. $P = 93.00, r = .06 \rightarrow Pe^{r} - 3e^{r/2} - 3 = 92.66$
$\rightarrow$ arbitrage opportunity

ii. $P = 92.38, r = .06 \rightarrow Pe^{r} - 3e^{r/2} - 3 = 92.00$
$\rightarrow$ no arbitrage opportunity

9.1.14 Since the delivery price one year from now is

$$1000 > 900e^{r} = 900e^{.10} = 994.65,$$

we have the following strategy:

(i) borrow 900 for one year at the risk-free rate of interest,

(ii) buy (one ounce) of gold now for 900,

(iii) take a short position in a one year forward contract on gold with delivery price 1000,

(iv) at the end of the year, sell the gold for 1000 to the long position holder of the forward contract,

(v) repay the loan, with payment 994.65.

Risk-free profit is $1000 - 994.65 = 5.35.$

9.1.15 Initial margin required is $(.05)(.55)(50,000) = 1,375$. The account balance the next day is $1,375 - (.10)(50,000) = 875$, and the margin required is $(.05)(.56)(50,000) = 1,400$. The farmer must add 525 to the account to maintain the margin.

9.1.16 (a) 1-year swap price for platinum is the same as the 1-year forward price of 1050.

2-year swap price P_2 is the solution of the equation

$$P_2 \times \left[\frac{1}{1.06} + \frac{1}{(1.065)^2} \right] = \frac{1050}{1.06} + \frac{1100}{(1.065)^2},$$

so that $P_2 = 1074.15$.

3-year swap price P_3 is the solution of the equation

$$P_3 \times \left[\frac{1}{1.06} + \frac{1}{(1.065)^2} + \frac{1}{(1.0675)^3} \right]$$
$$= \frac{1050}{1.06} + \frac{1100}{(1.065)^2} + \frac{1150}{(1.0675)^3},$$

so that $P_3 = 1097.71$.

4-year swap price P_4 is the solution of the equation

$$P_4 \times \left[\frac{1}{1.06} + \frac{1}{(1.065)^2} + \frac{1}{(1.0675)^3} + \frac{1}{(1.07)^4} \right]$$
$$= \frac{1050}{1.06} + \frac{1100}{(1.065)^2} + \frac{1150}{(1.0675)^3} + \frac{1100}{(1.07)^4},$$

so that $P_4 = 1098.22$.

(b)   The counterparty enters into long forward contracts to buy platinum at 1050, 1100, 1150 and 1100 at times 1, 2, 3, and 4. The counterparty's net payoffs at times 1, 2, 3, and 4 are

$(1098.22 - \text{spot}) + (\text{spot} - 1050) = 48.22$ at time 1,

$(1098.22 - \text{spot}) + (\text{spot} - 1100) = -1.78$ at time 2,

$(1098.22 - \text{spot}) + (\text{spot} - 1150) = -51.78$ at time 3,

$(1098.22 - \text{spot}) + (\text{spot} - 1100) = -1.78$ at time 4.

The present value of these cashflows is

$$\frac{48.22}{1.06} - \frac{1.78}{(1.065)^2} - \frac{51.78}{(1.0675)^3} - \frac{1.78}{(1.07)^4} = 0.$$

(c)   From the term structure, the forward rates of interest are

$$r_0(1,2) = \frac{(1.065)^2}{1.06} - 1 = .0700 \quad \text{from time 1 to time 2,}$$

$$r_0(2,3) = \frac{(1.0675)^3}{(1.065)^2} - 1 = .0725 \quad \text{from time 2 to time 3, and}$$

$$r_0(3,4) = \frac{(1.07)^4}{(1.0675)^3} - 1 = .0775 \quad \text{from time 3 to time 4.}$$

The value of the swap at time 0 is 0. There is a fixed payment of 1098.22 at time 1, which is an "overpayment" of $1098.22 - 1050 = 48.22$. This grows to $48.22(1.07) = 51.60$ (using the forward rate from time 1 to time 2).

The next swap payment is an underpayment, $1098.22 - 1100 = -1.78$. The amortized balance at time 2 after the swap payment is $51.60 - 1.78 = 49.82$. This grows to $49.82(1.0725) = 53.43$ at time 3,
and then there is an underpayment at time 3, $1098.22 - 1150 = -51.78$, for a net balance of $53.43 - 51.78 = 1.65$. This grows to $1.65(1.0775) = 1.78$ at time 4, and there is an underpayment at time 4 of $1098.22 - 1100 = -1.78$.

The net balance after the swap payment at time 4 is 0.

(d) The swap price for the deferred swap is P, where

$$P \times \left[\frac{1}{(1.0675)^3} + \frac{1}{(1.07)^4} \right] = \frac{1150}{(1.0675)^3} + \frac{1100}{(1.07)^4}$$

so that $P = 1125.93$.

(e) The value of the swap to the counterparty at time 1 is the present value (using the new term structure) of the difference between the swap price and the time 1 forward prices at times 2, 3 and 4. This is

$$\frac{1098.22 - 1150}{1.065} + \frac{1098.22 - 1200}{(1.07)^2} + \frac{1098.22 - 1300}{(1.07)^3} = -302.20.$$

9.1.17 We will denote the 1, 2, 3 and 4 year forward prices $F_{0,1}$, $F_{0,2}$, $F_{0,3}$, and $F_{0,4}$.

The 1-year swap price is the same as the one year forward price of 1100.

The 2-year swap price P_2 is the solution of the equation

$$P_2 \times \left[\frac{1}{1.06} + \frac{1}{(1.065)^2} \right] = \frac{F_{0,1}}{1.06} + \frac{F_{0,2}}{(1.065)^2} = \frac{1100}{1.06} + \frac{F_{0,2}}{(1.065)^2}.$$

From the given value of $P_2 = 1150$ we get $F_{0,2} = 1203.50$.

The 3-year swap price P_3 is the solution of the equation

$$P_3 \times \left[\frac{1}{1.06} + \frac{1}{(1.065)^2} + \frac{1}{(1.0675)^3} \right]$$

$$= \frac{F_{0,1}}{1.06} + \frac{F_{0,2}}{(1.065)^2} + \frac{F_{0,3}}{(1.0675)^3} .$$

$$= \frac{1100}{1.06} + \frac{1203.50}{(1.065)^2} + \frac{F_{0,3}}{(1.0675)^3}$$

The 4-year swap price P_4 is the solution of the equation

$$P_4 \times \left[\frac{1}{1.06} + \frac{1}{(1.065)^2} + \frac{1}{(1.0675)^3} + \frac{1}{(1.07)^4} \right]$$

$$= \frac{F_{0,1}}{1.06} + \frac{F_{0,2}}{(1.065)^2} + \frac{F_{0,3}}{(1.0675)^3} + \frac{F_{0,4}}{(1.07)^4}$$

$$= \frac{1100}{1.06} + \frac{1203.50}{(1.065)^2} + \frac{1150}{(1.0675)^3} + \frac{F_{0,4}}{(1.07)^3}.$$

From the given value of $P_4 = 1200$, we get $F_{0,4} = 1373.49$.

SECTIONS 9.2 AND 9.3

9.2.1   Let P denote the stock price on July 20.

(a) Profit $= P - 111$ if $P \geq 110$ (option is exercised on July 20)

Profit $= -1$ if $P \leq 110$ (option not exercised)

9.2.2   If damage is greater than 2000, up to 500,000, the insurance pays the damage amount minus 2000. Another way of describing this is that if the value of the house after damage is S_1 and is between 0 and 498,000, the insurance pays the amount by which the value of the car is below 498,000, so the insurance pays $Max\{498,000,0\} - 1000$. This is the payoff at the end of the year of a purchased option with a strike price of 498,000. The profit on the insurance policy would be $Max\{498,000 - S_1, 0\} - 1000$.

9.2.3   (a) $r = \ln\left(\frac{2100}{2000}\right) = .0488$

(b) Gain:

$$2100 - 80e^{.0488} - Min(2050, P) = 2016 - Min(2050, P).$$

9.2.4   (i)   If $S_1 \le X - C$ then call option will not be exercised; total gain is $S_1 - X + C \le 0$

(ii)   If $X - C < S_1 \le X$ then call option will not be exercised; total gain is $S_1 - X + C > 0$

(iii)   If $S_1 > X$, then call option will be exercised; total gain is $X - X + C = C > 0.$

9.2.5   Value of the forward contract at time T:
$$S_T - X.$$

Value of long put option with strike price X:
$$\max(X - S_T, 0).$$

Value of short put option with strike price X:
$$-\max(X - S_T, 0) = \min(S_T - X, 0).$$

Value of long call option with strike price X:
$$\max(S_T - X, 0).$$

Value of short call option with strike price X:
$$-\max(S_T - X, 0) = \min(X - S_T, 0).$$

Short put combined with long call has value at time T of:
$$\min(S_T - X, 0) + \max(S_T - X, 0) = S_T - X.$$

Answer: a

9.2.6 (a) The payoff at time 1 is payoff on stock + payoff on purchased
$$\text{put} = S_1 + \begin{cases} 50 - S_1 & \text{if } S_1 \le 50 \\ 0 & \text{if } S_1 > 50 \end{cases} = \begin{cases} 50 & \text{if } S_1 \le 50 \\ S_1 & \text{if } S_1 > 50 \end{cases} = Max\{50, S_1\}.$$

Total cost at time 0 is \$51.40 and accumulated value at time 1 is \$53.98.

The profit at time 1 is payoff minus 53.98 which is
$$\begin{cases} -3.98 & \text{if } S_1 \le 50 \\ S_1 - 53.98 & \text{if } S_1 > 50 \end{cases}.$$

(b) For strike price 30 we see that $S_0 + P_0 = 40 + 1.50 = 41.50$
and $C_0 + Ke^{-rT} = 12.92 + 30e^{-.05} = 41.46$
(the difference due to roundoff).

(c) The payoff is

$$Max\{S_1-42,0\} - Max\{S_1-50,0\} = \begin{cases} 0 & \text{if } S_1 \le 42 \\ S_1 - 42 & \text{if } 42 < S_1 \le 50 \\ 8 & \text{if } S_1 > 50 \end{cases}$$

The cost of the spread at time 0 is $6.34 - 3.78 = 2.56$ and the accumulated cost at time 1 is 2.69. The profit is payoff minus

$$2.69 = \begin{cases} -2.69 & \text{if } S_1 \le 42 \\ S_1 - 44.69 & \text{if } 42 < S_1 \le 50. \\ 5.31 & \text{if } S_1 > 50 \end{cases}$$

(d) The collar consists of a purchased put 40 and a written call 50. The payoff is

$$Max\{40-S_1,0\} - Max\{S_1-50,0\} = \begin{cases} 40 - S_1 & \text{if } S_1 \le 40 \\ 0 & \text{if } 40 < S_1 \le 50 \\ 50 - S_1 & \text{if } S_1 > 50 \end{cases}$$

The cost at time 0 for the collar is $5.28 - 3.78 = 1.50$ and the accumulated cost at time 1 is 1.58. The profit at time 1 is

$$\begin{cases} 38.42 - S_1 & \text{if } S_1 \le 40 \\ 0 & \text{if } 40 < S_1 \le 50. \\ 48.42 - S_1 & \text{if } S_1 > 50 \end{cases}$$

The payoff on the long stock is S_1 and the profit is $S_1 - 42.05$.

The payoff on the collared stock is $\begin{cases} 40 & \text{if } S_1 \leq 40 \\ S_1 & \text{if } 40 < S_1 \leq 50, \\ 50 & \text{if } S_1 > 50 \end{cases}$

and the profit is $\begin{cases} -3.63 & \text{if } S_1 \leq 40 \\ 0 & \text{if } 40 < S_1 \leq 50. \\ 6.37 - S_1 & \text{if } S_1 > 50 \end{cases}$

9.2.7 The payoff at maturity is $Max\left\{1.011, .75 \times \dfrac{S_T}{19.78}\right\}$, which can be written in the form $1.011 + .0379 \times Max\{0, S_T - 26.66\}$. At continuously compounded risk-free rate 5%, the value on August 11, 2006 is $1.011e^{-2.44(.05)} + .0379 \times C_0$, where C_0 is the premium of a call option on AMD with strike 26.7. From the AMD call option prices in Figure 9.3, we see that the call with strike 26.7 expiring in January 2009 is between 5.30 and 3.60, approximately 4.80. The cost of the hedge is approximately

$$1.011e^{-2.44(.05)} + .0379 \times 4.80 = 1.08.$$

9.2.8 (i) $\alpha = \dfrac{0 - 10}{144 - 100} = -.2273,$

$\beta = \dfrac{1}{1.11}\left[0 - \left(\dfrac{0 - 10}{144 - 100}\right)(144)\right] = 29.75.$

(ii) The replicating portfolio has $\alpha = \dfrac{24 - 0}{144 - 100} = .5455$ shares of stock and $\beta = \dfrac{1}{1.1}\left[24 - \left(\dfrac{24 - 0}{144 - 100}\right)(144)\right] = -49.59$ units of bond at risk-free rate.

Sell short .5455 shares, receive $(120)(.5455) = 65.46$. Buy the call for 15 and invest the remaining 50.46 at the risk-free interest rate.

At time 1:
- If the stock goes to 100, don't exercise the call; investment value is $(50.46)(1.1) = 55.50$; buy .5455 shares of stock for 54.55, with gain of .95;
- If stock goes to 144, exercise option for net amount 24, investment value is 55.50, buy .5455 shares for

$$(.5455)(144) = 78.55;$$

net position is

$$24 + 55.50 - 78.55 = .95.$$

9.2.9 (a) $K = 45 \rightarrow C_0 = 4.83$
$K = 50 \rightarrow C_0 = 2.75$
$K = 55 \rightarrow C_0 = 1.45$

9.2.10

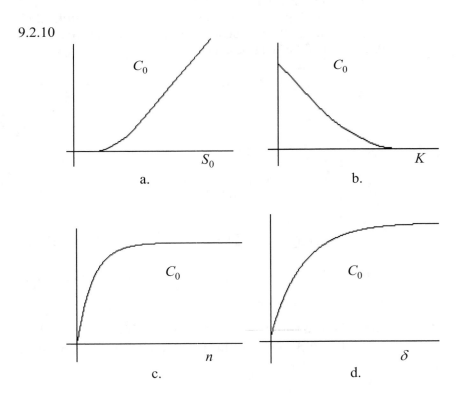

a.

b.

c.

d.

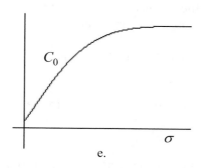

e.

SECTION 9.4

9.4.1   (a) $1.38(1.09) = (1+i)(1.42) \rightarrow i = .0593$

      (b) $X(1.10) = 1.38(1.09) \rightarrow X = 1.3675$

9.4.2   The 1-year forward value of the Canadian dollar is

$$.625e^{(.02-.03)} = .61878US.$$

The following strategy will result in an arbitrage gain: At time 0:

(i)   Borrow $.61878e^{-.02} = .60653US$ and invest at continuously compounded rate .02 for one year, and

(ii)   Enter forward contract to purchase Canadian dollars for .61878US in one year.

If the speculator is correct, and the Canadian dollar is worth .65US at time 1, then at time 1:

(i)   US dollar investment has grown to .61878US, so use this to buy a Canadian dollar when the forward contract is completed, then

(ii) Sell the Canadian dollar for .65US (assuming the prediction was correct), and

(iii) Repay .61878US on the US loan.

Net gain is $.65 - .61878 = .03122$ for net investment of 0.

9.4.3 Under current exchange rates, the current spot rate for one British Pound in terms of Canadian Dollar:

$$\text{UK £1} = \frac{1}{.7090} \times 1.5887 = \text{CDN } \$2.2563.$$

The one-year forward exchange rate for one British Pound in terms of Canadian Dollar:

$$\text{UK £1} = \frac{1}{.7200} \times 1.6100 = \text{CDN } \$2.2361.$$

Domestic currency is Canadian Dollar.

$$K = S_0 e^{(r-r_f)T} = S_0 \cdot \frac{1+i}{1+i_f} \rightarrow 2.2361$$

$$= 2.2563 \cdot \frac{1.02}{1+j} \rightarrow j = .0292.$$

9.4.4 (a) $K = S_0 e^{(r-r_f)T} \rightarrow 1.540 = (1.545)e^{(.06-r_f)(1)}$
$\rightarrow r_f = .0632$ is the implied US risk-free one-year continuously compounded rate of interest.

(b) Buy low sell high.

Sell today a one-year forward contract in US dollar with delivery price 1.55.

Borrow CDN $\dfrac{1.54}{e^{.06}} = 1.4503$ today and

buy US $\dfrac{1.4503}{1.545} = .9387$ at today's spot rate for US$.

Invest US $.9387 at US risk-free rate of .0632. At the end of 1 year, you have US $.9387 \times e^{.0632} = 1.000$; complete the forward contract by selling the US dollar and receive CDN $1.55. Repay the CDN $ loan with a payment of CDN $1.54. Profit of CDN $.01.

9.4.5   Under current exchange rates, the current spot rate for one US dollar in terms of Japanese Yen:

$$US\,\$1 = 1.5589 \times \frac{1}{.014200} = JP\,¥\,109.782.$$

The one-year forward exchange rate for one US dollar in terms of Japanese Yen:

$$US\,\$1 = 1.5495 \times \frac{1}{.014997} = JP\,¥\,103.321$$

(JP ¥ is now the "domestic" currency).

$$K = S_0 e^{(r-r_f)T} = S_0 \cdot \frac{1+i}{1+i_f}$$

$$\rightarrow\ 103.321 = 109.782 \cdot \frac{1+i}{1+.0613}\ \rightarrow\ i = -.0012.$$